FIGHTING FIT

EDDIE FERRIE

The Crowood Press

First published in 1990 by
The Crowood Press
Ramsbury, Marlborough,
Wiltshire SN8 2HE

British Library Cataloguing in Publication Data

Ferrie, Eddie
  Fighting fit.
  1. Physical fitness. Combat sports
  I. Title
  613.7'1

  ISBN 1 85223 323 0

Line-drawings by Vanetta Joffe

Typeset by Inforum Typesetting, Portsmouth
Printed in Great Britain by Redwood Burn Ltd, Trowbridge

Contents

Eddie Ferrie's involvement in the martial arts has included four years as a member of Britain's national judo squad and winning a gold medal in the Spanish Open in 1981. He has trained extensively in a variety of disciplines, especially ju-jitsu, karate, judo (in which he is a 3rd Dan) and both full-contact (Olympic) and semi-contact taekwondo.

As a full-time author and photographer, Eddie Ferrie contributes regularly to martial arts columns for national newspapers such as the *Guardian* and the *Daily Mail*. He has also written for *British Judo* and is the author of **Jujitsu, Judo for Self-Defence** and **Taekwondo** (all Crowood titles).

Introduction

Fitness is once again in vogue, and people from all walks of life are increasingly conscious of the need to look after themselves; to get and stay physically fit in order to improve their health and live fuller, more satisfying lives. One aspect of the fitness boom has been the growth in popularity of the oriental martial arts and their development into more sports-orientated forms, together with the realisation that these activities are not only useful methods of self-defence, but that they help promote and maintain very high levels of fitness. Many people come looking for alternatives to monotonous, one-dimensional activities like jogging or bodybuilding, and turn to training in martial arts and combat sports for the healthy exercise they provide which develops rounded, usable fitness. This book aims to explain the fitness benefits of involvement in a martial art or combat sport, and also to help those already involved to improve their performance capabilities by offering a variety of training options and a range of supplementary exercises.

Fighting Fit also aims to give the reader interested in training for combat sports all the information he needs to get himself into condition, whether he wants merely to be able to practise and enjoy his chosen discipline at club level, or has ambitions to become a champion. It is not possible to give tailored fitness programmes for the various martial arts and combat sports; that is the task of the instructor or the more experienced self-trained individual once he has assessed and ascertained his own level of fitness and his needs. This book does, however, provide all the information necessary to make that assessment.

Training methods and programmes which have proved successful at beginner, intermediate and advanced level in a variety of combat sports have been included as guides to help the trainee to see how certain results can be obtained, and it is hoped that the multi-disciplinary approach that has been adopted will help shed a little light and perhaps foster a spirit of mutual understanding among the devotees of activities at once so different and yet so similar in terms of the demands they make on the practitioners, as judo, karate, wrestling, kickboxing and taekwondo.

1 Fighting Fit

FIT FOR WHAT?

While most people have a general idea of what they mean by 'fitness', it is in fact a very vague term which only becomes specific in the context of a particular activity. The man who jogs a couple of miles 2 or 3 times a week and plays an occasional game of football, squash or cricket probably considers himself reasonably fit, and for the life he leads, he probably is. The powerlifter who can bench press over 180kg (400lb) but cannot comfortably run a mile is unlikely to be worried; similarly the marathon runner who can cover 26 miles in 2½ hours yet cannot lift his own bodyweight. They are fit for their sport but their fitness is likely to be of a limited, one-dimensional nature.

Combat sports are particularly demanding in that the kind of fitness they require is multi-component. The fighter, whatever his discipline, needs to be strong, fast, supple, capable of enduring and absorbing shocks and knocks, and skilful. Activities such as judo, karate, kickboxing, wrestling, taekwondo and their innumerable variants all promote and demand high levels of fitness, but the balance of the component elements is as different as the activities themselves.

Perhaps the most overlooked aspect of fit-

Fig 1   Judo: a sport that requires a wide range of abilities, including knowing how to fall. Neil Adams throws Chris Bowles with tai otoshi.

Fig 2   Kickboxing, perhaps the hardest of all combat sports.

ness training is the psychological one. There is a mountain of readily available – albeit at times conflicting – material on physical conditioning, on how to become fitter, stronger and more supple, but in combat sports psychological preparedness is just as important as physical form. One key element in this is exercise enjoyment: if the trainee enjoys the training he will continue with it and almost inevitably improve; also, if the training stimulates and satisfies him, much more enjoyment and fulfilment should derive from actual competition. A large part of getting the mind right is, of course, getting the body fit first: it is easier to be relaxed and confident prior to a big event if you know you are at your peak of fitness and strength.

It is particularly important when training to improve your performance in a combat sport to get the balance of the different components right. Any analysis of the components of fighting fitness soon reveals that they are inextricably interlinked, affecting one another and depending upon one another far more than the average trainee realises.

HOW FIT ARE YOU?

Again, 'fit' is such an unspecific word that training to get fit covers everything from physical therapy to athletic performance under contest conditions. Within the general concept of fitness there are a number of categories which are determined by a variety of components. The first question you should ask yourself before attempting to assess your own level of fitness is, how fit do I need to be? If you are 35 years old and have started training in a combat sport 2 or 3 times a week

7

in order to lose half a stone, the answer will be very different to that of a 22 year-old judo player aspiring to the Olympic games. A useful definition of fitness is the ability to perform and continue performing at a given level. The absolute peak condition of the Olympic athlete far exceeds the needs or aspirations of the average trainee, but that fact need not devalue your own sense of self-worth. Since fitness is basically the ability to perform a task, the nature of the task is what determines how fit you need to be. If you aim to be a competitive wrestler, whether you can run a marathon or not may be largely irrelevant to your fitness to wrestle. Certainly, attaining the necessary level of fitness to be able to run a marathon does not prepare you to go in the ring with a kickboxer.

Fitness should not be confused with health. It is possible to be extremely fit but not healthy, and vice versa. An Olympic athlete stands the same chance of dying of cancer as the totally untrained person, although the person who never does any exercise has a much higher chance of dying of heart-disease than the athlete. Being fit is no defence against many types of illness or disease. Illness, whether trivial as in the case of a cold or a tummy bug, or more serious, such as bronchitis or pneumonia, will invariably have an adverse effect on fitness. It is particularly inadvisable to train when ill. The notion of sweating out a cold is potentially dangerous, both to yourself and others, in as much as others might catch your cold, and you might end up with glandular fever if the cold turns out to be more serious than you thought.

TYPES OF FITNESS

Cardiovascular Fitness

(Aerobic capacity or endurance). This is what people usually mean by the term 'fitness'. In a very general sense it is the capacity to keep going when doing physical exercise or work. This basic heart-lung fitness determines your physical work capacity to a large extent. In many ways it is the easiest area to improve, since it simply involves getting the heart rate up to a level where there is a training effect and keeping it there. This training effect is normally achieved by working at between 70 and 80 per cent of your maximum heart rate.

The most basic type of training used to bring about improved endurance is often referred to as 'steady state' training, because the trainee reaches a sustainable level of exercise intensity and works at that level for a predetermined period of time. Jogging, swimming, skipping, rowing and cycling are all excellent steady state activities. Steady state work is rhythmical and should be the foundation for any fitness programme for the previously untrained and unfit. When done correctly it is, because of the gently increasing demands it places on the body, one of the safest and most effective ways to improve fitness. It is sometimes referred to as low intensity training; however, even low intensity work has to be progressive in order to continue to be of value.

One method of assessing your current level of fitness is to use the pulse rate as a guide. The first step is to ascertain your maximum heart rate, in order to work out what your working pulse rate should be (i.e. the 70 to 80 per cent of your maximum heart rate already referred to). This is done simply by subtracting your age from the figure 220. Thus, a 30 year-old will have a maximum heart rate of 190, whereas a 40 year-old's would be 170, and a 20 year-old's would be 200. Consequently, a 20 year-old wanting to exercise at 70 to 80 per cent would need to do sufficient work to get his pulse between 140 and 160. The formula to find the minimum rate at which your heart must work to get a training effect is to subtract your age from 220 and multiply that number first by 70 per cent and then by 80 per cent, and you have the upper and lower ranges between which you should keep your heart working. In order to improve basic aerobic fitness you have to get your heart in to this range and keep it there for a minimum of 12 minutes, bearing in mind that increasing the duration of the activity by anything up to an hour will bring increased fitness. Exceeding 1½ hours is of little relevance to the martial artist generally and is really the domain of specialist endurance athletes such as marathon runners and cyclists.

This, of course, presupposes a reasonable level of fitness as a result of previous training. A totally unfit person or complete beginner would be advised to do an 8-week programme training at about 60 per cent. Attempting to go straight in at the higher level of intensity could be both unpleasant and dangerous. Fitness programmes should always be geared to the individual.

It is also advisable to determine your resting pulse rate. This is best taken early in the morning before you get out of bed. (Incidentally, if at any time you feel you may be suffering from overtraining, taking your pulse in this way in the morning can give you an indication. A higher than normal resting pulse rate is a sure sign you are doing too much, and a couple of days complete rest should be taken to allow it to return to normal. This only applies, of course, if you have been training hard and you know what your normal resting pulse rate should be.) To take your pulse, place your fingertips – not your thumb – on the thumb side of your wrist, palm facing up. Count the number of beats in one minute, using a watch for the purpose. For rapid monitoring purposes you can count the number of pulse beats in 15 seconds and multiply by 4, but until you have some experience, take a minute. The national average is about 72 for a man and 84 for a woman. In the case of trained athletes, generally the lower the pulse rate, the higher the index of aerobic fitness. Top middle-distance runners, for instance, frequently have pulse rates in the 30s and 40s. Many simple fitness tests use the time taken for the heart to return to its normal resting pulse rate after exercise as an indicator of fitness.

This description of basic exercise physiology is necessary since ignorance of what constitutes a training effect is surprisingly widespread. A common mistake is to go on very long, slow jogs which do not get the heart rate up to an effective training rate. Such jogs have their uses, of course, helping to dispel lactic acid after training and burning excess calories being the most obvious, but they do little to improve actual cardiovascular efficiency except in the case of completely out-of-condition beginners, who, once they have developed their fitness to the point where they can run 5 miles in an hour, have to start going faster if they want to make any further improvement to their cardiovascular system.

Anaerobic Fitness

(Capacity to work without direct oxygen supply, necessary for maximum efforts). Anaerobic training is quite different to steady state training and will cause pulse rates close to maximum and large buildups of lactic acid in the muscles, accompanied by feelings of total fatigue and an inability to continue doing the activity. It is very demanding and should not be undertaken by anyone who has not reached a decent level of aerobic fitness first as the heart and lungs and the muscular system need to be in good condition, otherwise injury may result. Sprinting is a typical anaerobic activity, especially the 400-metre sprint which, done repetitively, is a gruelling but very effective way of improving the body's anaerobic system and tolerance of lactic acid. Often such a programme requires rest periods that are much longer than the actual time spent training. An athlete doing a sub 60-second 400-metres may need up to 5 minutes to recover. Anaerobic means working without direct oxygen supply from breathing, but for maximum efficiency,

9

both the body's energy systems need to be trained. Anaerobic fitness influences speed and power.

Muscular Fitness

This category comprises the capacity of the muscles to exert force, the speed at which they can exert that force, and the muscles' flexibility.

HOW STRONG ARE YOU?

Sheer strength is relevant in combat sports only to the extent that it can be expressed as speed (power), and the effectiveness of any explosive movements are determined by a variety of other factors including flexibility, relaxation and motor co-ordination. In calculating your strength you have to consider

Fig 3 The balanced physique of a karate athlete, the result of years of training: Gerry McElligott, Shotokan 4th dan.

Fig 4 Karateka do not have the bulging, showy muscles of the bodybuilder, but rather the long, supple muscles of the athlete, built for function not show. Left to right: M. Etienne, L. Fairclough and Ian Cole, British team members 1988.

used, as can free exercises which tend to display strength endurance rather than gross muscular power. Heavyweight wrestlers and judo players probably need more sheer strength than any other type of fighter.

HOW FAST ARE YOU?

Speed is a decisive element in all the combat sports and there are two types to consider in combat sports: reaction speed and movement speed. The fastest type of movement is a conditioned reflex developed through years of repetitive training. The simpler the movement the faster it can be done. There is no way a complex movement like a judo throw can ever be as quick as a simple punch, for instance. But in either case, top exponents of judo and karate tend to do very basic techniques in contest rather than the elaborate, superficially more complex actions. The effective sports karateka needs

Fig 5 L. Fairclough, European karate champion. Note the mid-section condition.

your power-to-weight ratio which relates your performance to your bodyweight. A 65kg (10st) man who can lift 95kg (15st) is relatively stronger than a 100kg (16st) man who can lift 115kg (18st), even though the heavier man has greater absolute strength. An important aspect of strength is strength endurance. Two fighters may be unequal in sheer power when a fight commences, but the less powerful one may end up being effectively stronger than his opponent by out-lasting him and wearing him down. Heavy, bulky fighters with big muscles may be tremendously powerful, but they have to supply those muscles with oxygen via the blood in order for them to keep working, which is where heart-lung fitness becomes important. Bigger muscle groups burn more energy at a faster rate; thus, fighters with big muscles may be impossible to overpower, but they can be tired out.

There are various ways to measure strength. Machines and free weights can be

Fig 6 Karate: speed, timing and flexibility combine with flawless technique in this side kick attack by Jose Agea of Spain, 6 times European karate champion.

11

Fig 7   Taekwondo is a sport where the high kicking techniques are among the most spectacular of all.

razor-sharp reflexes and lightning-fast technique. The boxer, kickboxer and taekwondo fighter, too, need to be able to beat their opponents to the score to be really effective. Judo and wrestling bouts also are frequently decided by virtue of superior speed. 'Speed wins', to quote a famous saying from the judo world.

Tension and stiffness tend to prevent fast movement, and to perform techniques well under pressure the timing has to be right and the athlete must be able to relax. It was once said of judo champion Neil Adams, who was capable of throwing his opponents when seemingly locked in the sort of battle for grips that normally preclude the possibility of any effective technique, that 'He relaxed faster than everyone else.' A lot of other great champions share this quality: Vic Charles in the karate world, Jimmy Kim from taek-

wondo, and any number of top boxers from Muhammad Ali to Sugar Ray Leonard.

HOW FLEXIBLE ARE YOU?

Flexibility is an important consideration in most of the combat sports, but of course the areas where a person needs to be flexible are determined by the specific activity. The semi-contact taekwondo fighter requires extreme hip and hamstring flexibility in order to perform the spectacular high kicking techniques which are germane to the art, while the ordinary boxer has no need for such extreme flexibility in the lower limbs, requiring rather to keep supple in the shoulders, torso and back. A flexible fighter is more efficient, and flexibility is vital for the avoidance of injury. Injuries are frequently the result of muscles and joints being stretched beyond their normal range of motion; the greater that range in the first place the less likely an injury is to occur. Flexibility leads to mobility and mobility to technical effectiveness.

HOW SKILFUL ARE YOU

Fitness and skill are crucially interlinked in a number of ways. Skills and the speed at which they can be performed are limited by three major factors: the rate of muscle contraction, which is to some extent determined by the proportion of fast and slow twitch muscle fibres in the body; internal resistance resulting from a lack of relaxation and suppleness in muscles, ligaments and joints; and muscular co-ordination. The normal training methodology of most martial arts recognises this and consequently repetition plays an extremely important part in skill acquisition. Some modernists concerned purely with physical conditioning argue that performing extremely high numbers of repetitions is meaningless and monotonous, but for many people this is the only way to develop the neuro-muscular co-ordination necessary in order to perform the techniques they practise in the heat of a bout.

Skill allows power to be generated, whether expressed as a kick, punch or throw; it is characterised by a smooth co-ordinated action and can compensate for disadvantages like tiredness or differences in size and weight. It is very easy to go overboard on strength and endurance programmes, but the aim is to improve your performance in your particular sport, and the skill element in the end is the most important. The key to progress is to become fit and strong enough to be able to skill train effectively.

Skill can, however, be doubled-edged from the point of view of absolute fitness. In a competitive training situation, the more skilful individual is rarely taxed physically if left to his own devices, unless he is exceptionally self-motivating. He can usually achieve his objective in bringing off a scoring technique without using up too much energy, and therein lies the problem. Many very skilful, keen young fighters tend to train with people who are less competitive, less skilled and less demanding than the sort of opposition they encounter in competition, and it is difficult to improve in such an environment. It is vitally important to train and practise with people who are as good and indeed better than you are yourself if you have serious aspirations; even world champions need this kind of stimulus to retain their winning edge. Of course, psychology has an important role to play in all this. Some people are happy to be big fish in little ponds. They are often talented and skilful, which means they do not have to work so hard in training, but not talented and skilful enough to reach the top, certainly not without doing the necessary work.

Even so, ultimately there is no substitute for developing skill. When the highest levels of fitness are reached it is usually the more skilful fighters who take the medals, and after retirement from competition it is they who are able to carry on in the sport, becoming the coaches and teachers for the champions of the future.

Skill Analysis

Feedback from training partners and coaches is extremely useful in improving skills and eradicating faults in technique. Often you may be too close to a problem to be able to see it properly, but a coach or training partner can spot it almost immediately. Video can help you to see what you do when you are both training and competing – often there is quite a difference between what you think you are doing, and what you are actually doing! Video is also useful for studying the opposition, analysing opponents' performances, looking for strengths as well as weaknesses. It is even possible to learn new techniques this way. Yasuhiro Yamashita, the greatest judo champion of all time, used to study his opponents on video, poring over films of their past contests for hours until he discovered their weak points. Many fighters give a lot more away in contest than they do in training; as the Japanese say, 'You must steal with your eyes.'

13

2   Training Frameworks

HIERARCHY: BEGINNER TO BLACK BELT

One of the great advantages of martial arts and combat sports training is that it takes place in an extremely well structured hierarchical system. In most systems the beginner wears a white belt until having done sufficient training to take a grading, when, if successful, he can earn a belt denoting higher rank and competence. The standard aim for most beginners is the dan grade or black belt; however, this is really only an indication of competence of a very basic level rather than the ultimate goal. In karate and taekwondo, 4th degree black belt or 4th dan is the highest grade that can be attained for fighting ability and technical competence in most styles. In judo it is 5th dan. Within traditional systems grades beyond these are normally awarded by a panel of experts of the particular governing body.

Certain 'modern masters' give themselves grades which have no real objective value, only having any meaning within the confines of the particular school or system of that 'master'. An individual being awarded his 9th dan in any of the traditional schools would of necessity be a very old man. A 35 year-old Western karate teacher claiming to be a 10th dan needs to be considered from a different perspective. He will not necessarily be any better either as a performer or a teacher than someone who is a 4th dan in a traditional style, in fact he might well be considerably inferior. The point is that it is not always clear-cut when grades are compared, since the grades may denote quite different things in different systems.

The creation of the modern coloured belt systems was not of oriental origin, but rather a western development. In Japan, judoka and karateka tended to be either white, brown or black belts. Any Japanese taking up such an activity would understand that he was subjecting himself to a discipline which would last, potentially at least, a lifetime. Consequently there was no hurry to become a black belt, since competence is an almost inevitable consequence of commitment. For the Westerner, though, the belt ranking system is extremely important and a valuable motivational tool for instructors and students alike. The boost to the trainee's confidence and self-image which accompanies the transition from brown belt to black belt can be quite remarkable.

Champions frequently confound the belt ranking system, since among such strongly individualised types, medals and titles frequently take precedence over grades. Elvis Gordon, Britain's world silver medal winner at the 1987 World Judo Championships and European Champion in 1988, was a 1st dan at the time even though his actual standard of fighting ability could not be less than 5th dan having reached that level. Wolverhampton club mate Dennis Stewart took a bronze medal at the Seoul Olympics, and despite having trained at top level for over 10 years was a 1st dan at the time.

The beginner in judo, karate or taekwondo trains initially with the aim of getting the next belt. The belt ranking system varies considerably but usually comprises a number of coloured belts prior to black belt; then a succession of higher dan grades. The judo senior belt system is typical and goes from light to dark:

white – no grade
yellow – 9th kyu
orange – 8th kyu
orange – 7th kyu
green – 6th kyu
green – 5th kyu
blue – 4th kyu
blue – 3rd kyu
brown – 2nd kyu
brown – 1st kyu
black – 1st dan to 5th dan
red and white – 6th dan to 8th dan
red – 9th and 10th dan

The junior system is even more graded with 18 mon grades to be won, 3 white, 3 yellow, 3 orange, 3 green, 3 blue, and 3 brown. White belt with one red stripe is the absolute bottom, and brown belt with 3 red stripes, or 18th mon, is the highest belt for under 16s. There are no junior black belts in judo, unlike karate. A talented youngster must compete against adults if he wants to be graded to black belt – to quote Mike Tyson, the youngest ever World Heavyweight Boxing Champion, 'When you are good enough, you are old enough'. Anyone, senior or junior, wanting to go to the next grade in judo has to show technical knowledge, but must also fight other players of similar experience and win, in order to be graded up.

Karate and taekwondo have a similar system although there are some important differences, a red belt in taekwondo corresponds to a brown belt in judo or karate, and a purple belt in karate being the equivalent to blue in judo, and so on. Because karate techniques are inherently more dangerous and control more crucial than in judo, karate students are frequently not required to fight until they reach brown belt level, as the standard of control required to prevent accidents tends to be lacking before this level is reached.

As well as providing a hierarchy and an immediate visual indicator of an individual's level of experience, the belt system provides

Fig 8 Karate is an excellent acitivity for youngsters, where, unlike judo it is possible to become a blackbelt purely on the basis of technical merit.

the trainee with short-term goals, which are crucial in order to maintain enthusiasm and motivation. The goals a trainee or his coach sets have to be realistic and achievable and will vary enormously depending upon his talent and commitment. An athlete's capacity to succeed in any given activity is to a large extent determined by his genetic potential. As they say, 'You can't make a Derby winner out of a cart-horse.' But genetic potential is not the whole story. Psychological factors play just as important a part as physiological elements. There are so many variables within the scenario of combat that frequently the underdog can and does win against all the odds. Skill is not genetically predetermined, nor are fighting spirit and determination.

15

THE TRAINING DIARY

The training diary is an essential piece of equipment for monitoring your physical condition and can be an interesting record of achievement as well as a source of inspiration. Enter such details as your age, weight and pulse rate, and record of your personal best performances in the gym and in competition. Personal bests for running and lifting weights will vary considerably if, like many, you tend to go up and down in weight throughout the year. A 90kg (14½st) person in June can easily become a 95kg (15½st) one by December. Your time for running 3 miles will be slower in 99 per cent of cases if you put on weight, although you may expect a corresponding increase in sheer strength, pehaps an ability to handle considerably heavier weights. If the winters are harsh where you live, it can be prudent to synchronise your training effort with the seasons. Most people tend to eat more in cold weather, so it is a difficult time to control weight; especially with Christmas to compound the problem. Many fighters who have a tendency to bulk up in the winter months try to exploit the situation by doing a lot of indoor strength training and gymnasium work, building muscle, then, when spring comes, getting out on the track and burning off the surplus fat. This is a good example of positive mental attitude, turning what could be a disadvantage into an advantage. If you are going to bulk up anyway, far better muscle and fat than just fat! The alternative, of course, is to get to your ideal weight through a combination of training and diet and maintain that condition regardless of changes in climate. This requires strong self-discipline and a benevolent metabolism.

Use the diary to make notes on how individual training sessions felt, detailing the good and bad aspects, and indicating where you feel more work needs to be done. Record your eating habits and look for indications as to how different foods might affect your performance. One kickboxer who always trained better in summer than winter discovered that much better training sessions occurred on the summer days when he ate a lot of fruit 2 hours before training. In winter he tended to eat a hot dinner before training as he felt the cold sapped more of his energy. As an experiment he began eating fruit in November and December. Initially he felt deprived but then discovered pasta a good source of carbohydrate energy which he could eat hot, and he made great progress through the winter for the first time ever, at the same time keeping his weight stable instead of ballooning up as he normally did.

Another function of the training diary is to plot your immediate and long-term goals. It is important to have both as achieving the small goals makes it possible to realise the larger ones. First, decide what your goal for the year is. It might be to get a higher grade, to win a medal in a championship, to lose weight or master a new technique, or a combination of such things. Thus, a skinny brown belt in karate might have goals like these:

Gain half a stone by weight training and eating more.
Get fitter and sharper.
Develop effective left mawashigeri right gyaku zuki combination and ashi barai off the front foot.
Do 3 karate sessions per week and gain a black belt.

A judo player, already a black belt 2nd dan, who is left-handed and trains on the mat 4 times a week, having decided he is too light for his current weight category might plan the following:

Run 3 times a week in the mornings and lose half a stone.
Once weight is achieved work on speed and develop a throw on the right side.
Practise following up into ground work after throwing anyone in randori.

Win the North West area championships.
Win a medal in the British Championships.

Devising short-term goals makes it more interesting, too. The following might be a typical example of a 1st dan training for his 2nd dan grading in karate.

This week:
Monday, Wednesday and Friday: karate practice.
Work on hand and foot combinations. Monday and Wednesday: do extra 15 minutes' kata practice after session. Friday: extra practice on ashi-barai.
Tuesday and Thursday: running followed by weight-training circuit. Increase distance from 2½ miles to 3½ miles at 7-minute mile pace on Thursday. Raise weight in bench press by 2.5kg (5lb).
Saturday: swim half a mile
Sunday: rest.
Comments: Monday and Wednesday, karate felt good, fast and strong. Friday, legs a bit sore and stiff, took a long time to get warmed up but beat a black belt in free-sparring! Didn't have time to do proper warming down on Thursday night because the longer run took longer than expected, quite tired at 3 mile stage, only managed 7½-minute mile pace. Took a hard kick to the abdomen on Friday in sparring. Need to do more stomach work. Missed swim on Saturday because car broke down. Do a mile next week!

Things do not always go exactly according to plan; if circumstances beyond your control occasionally cause you to miss a session it is not the end of the world, just think how fresh you will be for the next session and work as hard as you can when it comes round. It is very important, however, not to miss training for trivial reasons, such as when you are tired.

It is a good idea, if you plan to compete seriously, to analyse opponents' strengths and weaknesses and make a record of them, too. A properly-kept training diary can be an invaluable source of reference and inspiration – every trainer should have one.

DIET AND WEIGHT CONTROL

Diet is a controversial area within sports science just as it is in life generally. Some scientists contend that diet plays absolutely no part whatsoever in improving athletic performance or otherwise, arguing that it really does not matter what you eat as long as you eat the required amount to provide the body with sufficient energy to supply the demands placed upon it by training.

It is commonly accepted now that dieting makes you fat, and not without reason. Radically cutting down food intake leads to the body actually converting muscle into energy to make up for the food supply it 'thinks' has been cut off. In famine conditions the body uses up muscle in preference to fat as a source of energy. Losing weight this way is not recommended for those intending to participate in combat sports or for anyone else for that matter; it is potentially very dangerous.

The best way to lose weight is to eat only slightly less than the amount required to maintain your current bodyweight, and to increase the amount of exercise you do. Eating 250 calories less per day and doing 250 calories' worth of exercise more give you a daily calorie reduction of 500, which, over the course of a week amounts to a 3,500 calorie deficit. This is the equivalent of a pound of fat, so proceeding in this fashion you could realistically expect to cut weight at the rate of one pound a week until reaching your optimum level. To indicate what little effort this involves, the trainee giving up 2½ cups of coffee (normally drunk with sugar and milk) and running 2 miles a day at about 9 miles an hour, would be on course. This is much easier than the alternative, which is to make a huge increase in exercising, say running 5 miles a day, and not modifying your diet, which also places greater demands on your capacity to recuperate and your time. Gaining weight obviously involves a reversal of the weight-loss procedure, taking in more calories than you use up. Again, this is best achieved by eating a little more every day and modifying your exercise habits – cut down on running, swimming and so on, and concentrate on heavy weights. Ensure the extra calories that you take in contain a balance of carbohydrates, proteins and fats. One useful fact to remember is that it takes about 15 calories per pound of bodyweight to maintain a given weight prior to calculating the energy cost of training. So a 80kg (13st) man in a sedentary occupation would need to consume 2,700 calories a day to stay at that weight. If he were training for a half-marathon though, running 10 miles a day or more, and he wanted to maintain his bodyweight, he would probably need to consume another 700–1,000 calories on top, otherwise he would lose weight rapidly. If you intend training hard to put weight on, make sure it is the right kind of training and monitor your fat levels to make sure you are not just putting on unnecessary fat. If you can pinch more than an inch on the hips, thighs and waistline, adjust your diet and routine accordingly.

Eating for Energy

There is a lot of conflicting information as to what food is required by the athlete in training. In the modern western world, with the wide availability of all kinds of food all the year round, it is hard to envisage a diet lacking in any of the essentials. The best piece of general advice is to eat a balanced, varied diet. Try to avoid eating the same food every day, and most importantly, eat what you enjoy as far as possible.

The 3 basic calorific elements of food are protein, carbohydrate and fat. Proteins are often considered to be the building blocks of the body's muscular system. The amount of protein the body requires even in heavy training is surprisingly low, about 1-1½g per kilogram of bodyweight. Excessive protein consumption serves no useful end, since once the body has the protein it requires it converts the extra and stores it as fat. The 80kg (13st) karateka trying to put on muscle needs about 80–100g (3–3½oz) of protein a day. The following are good sources of protein: meat, fish, poultry, eggs, milk, cheese, spinach, cauliflower, sprouts, soya, barley, nuts and bran. During heavy-weight training wheat-germ and brewer's yeast can provide good, easily assimilable sources of protein which contain the enzymes necessary to break down carbohydrates and fats for energy.

Carbohydrates are the most important source of food energy in the sportsman's diet. Poor performances, lack of energy or spring in the muscles and chronic tiredness which are frequently perceived to be the results of overtraining are more often the result of a depletion of carbohydrate stores in the muscles and liver. The sportsman in serious training ought to have a diet composed of at least 50 per cent carbohydrate, even when he intends to lose weight, as the 'carbs' provide the energy to exercise effectively and metabolise fat. Good sources of carbohydrate are: pasta, potatoes, bread, corn, honey, fruit, noodles, milk, flour, cereals, grains and sugar. Sugar needs to be handled with care as the timing of when you eat it is vital. Trainees often like to eat a pre-workout meal which will give them instant energy, but the body reacts by secreting insulin if you eat something with a high sugar content just before training. Insulin lowers blood sugar levels, which causes exactly the opposite reaction to the one you want. The same food eaten a few hours before training allows the insulin reaction to subside and the blood sugar level to rise.

Glycogen Loading

Carbohydrates can play an important role in a technique many athletes find helpful to boost their energy levels on a given day. Any exercise involves carbohydrates being burned as muscle glycogen. An athlete having 1.5 per cent glycogen content in his muscles is able to exercise at 75 per cent of maximum for up to 2 hours. During the training session or match the glycogen content of the muscle decreases. The phenomenon known in marathon running as 'hitting the wall', when the body reaches near total exhaustion, is a result of the body's having completely used up its store of glycogen from the liver and then being forced to use up the emergency glycogen supplies in the muscle. One way to pre-empt this is to increase the concentration of stored glycogen prior to the event. Glycogen stores can be increased by up to 50 per cent by carbohydrate loading. A carbohydrate-rich meal following an exhausting effort can increase the glycogen store by 4 per cent, but this effect can be enhanced by subjecting the body to a zero carbohydrate diet beforehand. The athlete eats only protein and fat for several days and then abruptly changes to a high carbohydrate diet, which results in inreased glycogen storage for up to 3 days.

To peak in this way for competition, the following regime is suggested. Five days before the contest the athlete has his last all-out workout, exhausting his glycogen supplies. He then goes on a high protein-low carbohydrate diet and does very light training for 3 days. Two days before the event he reverts to his high carbohydrate-low protein diet, and by the day of the contest his emergency glycogen store is 3–4 times higher than normal. This can be crucially important if the athlete has to fight a series of contests over the course of a day, which can be just as gruelling as pure endurance events like the marathon. Naturally this dietary strategy must be tested in training in order to see exactly how your individual metabolism responds to the treatment, but the potential for fighters is considerable.

Fats, too, play their part in a balanced diet, being highly concentrated sources of energy. Fat sources can be animal or vegetable, although the latter receive much better press in the current climate of medical opinion and function in much the same way as carbohydrates. Polyunsaturated fats are healthier than saturated fats, which can lead to buildups of cholesterol in the arteries. Low-fat spreads are consequently felt to be preferable to butter, but there is little need to subject oneself to the tyranny of a totally fat-free diet. Fats are especially useful in cold climates for helping the body to store energy and retain heat.

Water is crucial to the normal function of the body. Attempting to alter the body's water balance in order to achieve a lower weight category for a competition is draining, and the athlete is likely to be tired and unable to perform at his best as a result. He would be better advised to have his weight properly under control at all times. Fluid loss through sweating ought to be replaced by drinking water, particularly in hot conditions where dehydration may result.

Minerals and vitamins tend to be taken care of by a balanced diet. Green vegetables and fruit are very good sources, hence the popularity of the salad with many sportspeople. Although mineral and vitamin supplements are commercially available it is almost impossible to envisage a diet which, while supplying the necessary carbohydrates, fats and proteins, would lack any of the necessary minerals and vitamins. However, taking vitamin pills can have an important placebo effect on some fighters.

3 Basic Fitness

Although training in a combat sport is a very good way to get fit in its own right, it is generally a good idea to pre-condition yourself prior to starting training. This applies to experienced, perhaps older trainees returning to the sport after a lay-off just as much as it does to novices. Beginners' courses generally provide just the preconditioning you need to go on to the more demanding full sessions, but even these can be more enjoyable if you get yourself fit for them first. There are a number of basic activities which can promote and develop physical fitness, one of the most popular being running. The beginner starts out walking and jogging, the marathon man covers 26 miles at 5-minute mile pace, while the sprint athlete performs incredibly gruelling 400-metre repetition sprints that leave him scarcely able to walk, but there are a host of routines and training methods between these extremes.

A viable alternative to running for the overweight is the stationary exercise bike, common equipment in almost every gym these days. It is, however, monotonous and unless the trainee is highly motivated his enthusiasm is likely to wear out before the bike does. Rowing machines are similarly useful and give the body a more varied workout, getting the arms and back involved in the exercise, too. Skipping is another good basic exercise for improving the cardiovascular system.

Gym routine for the beginner. To be done 3 times per week for a month.
3 minutes skipping
3 minutes exercise bike
3 minutes jogging machine
3 minutes rowing machine
This is then repeated. Note that each 3-minute block of work can be followed by a 1-minute rest period in the first week, reduced to 45 seconds in the second week, 30 seconds in the third week and 15 seconds in the fourth week. After 4 weeks it should be possible, though certainly not easy, for the average trainee to do the exercises without resting. Add some stretching exercises and 3 sets of 10 repetitions of callisthenic exercises such as press-ups, squat thrusts, leg raises, burpees, dips and chins, and you have a good workout for intermediate level trainers up to 1st dan standard. This is a good routine for weight reduction also, as it burns a lot of calories and effectively speeds up the metabolism. Music can be helpful to develop rhythm for skipping and can provide inspiration when going through such routines.

Perhaps the best cardiovascular exercise, which incidentally also tones the muscles, is swimming. It is one of the most difficult exercises for which to set times and distances with any accuracy. However, since speed in the water is determined by a number of factors such as drag, tissue density, flexibility, stroke efficiency, breathing efficiency and so on. The best way to approach training in the water is in terms of your own best efforts. A fit karateka or boxer might take 3 minutes to swim 100 metres, while someone of inferior ability and physical condition who has better buoyancy and breathing technique, or is simply a better swimmer, might do the same distance in 2 minutes. Swimming is a skill like any other: the better swimmer will not necessarily be the fitter athlete.

There are two simple approaches to using swimming to get fit. The first is to pick a stroke (usually breast-stroke or crawl) and swim for a minimum of 20 minutes 3 times a week.

However, if you do not monitor your heart-beat it becomes all too easy to work below your optimum training rate. A more certain approach is to alternate strokes, say breast-stroke and crawl, and do a simple kind of interval swimming. Good swimmers can do a length breast-stroke at a relaxed rate and alternate with a length front crawl swimming flat out. The heart rate shoots up as a result of the high-speed efforts and the swimmer recovers on the easier breast-stroke length. Twenty minutes of this can be exhausting and amounts to good, quality training. Less accomplished swimmers who perhaps have problems getting their breathing right on front crawl can swim widths instead. The ratio of flat-out lengths to easy lengths can be adjusted depending upon fitness. One-to-one is extremely hard, two easy lengths to one fast one effectively increases the trainee's recovery time and is suggested for those at intermediate level. The untrained and not very fit can begin working at a 3-to-1 ratio, aiming for 1-to-1 after 3 months while training 3 times a week. Effective results can be obtained by experimenting with the stroke rate: as well as swimming flat out, try swiming at 70, 80 and 90 per cent of top speed, which can be ascertained by timing yourself over given distances.

TYPES OF TRAINING

There are two basic types of training: steady state training, sometimes referred to as low intensity work, and high intensity training which by its very nature results in the necessity for interval training. Obviously the best way to run 100 metres faster than before is to keep training at the kind of speed required by the event, or faster (hence the existence of events like the 60-metres dash which many top sprinters find helpful for fine tuning and improving their speed out of the blocks and pick up), but the problem is that bursts of high speed cannot be sustained long enough for a satisfactory training effect. To put it another way, it is impossible to sprint a mile, but you can do 15 x 100 metres at speeds near your best provided you allow yourself sufficient recovery time between efforts.

Interval training is one of the best methods of training for speed although it can be modified to enhance endurance. The training effect is determined by manipulating the following variables:

1. Speed
2. Distance covered
3. Number of repetitions
4. Rest period between efforts

Using running as the training medium for improving leg speed and high intensity fitness, a typical schedule might entail doing 8 x 400-metre dashes, aiming to complete each dash in 70–80 seconds and resting during the time taken to slowly walk a lap – perhaps 5 minutes. Speed and recovery time are obviously determined by current levels of fitness. Before and after such high-speed work a thorough warm-up and stretch is recommended.

A similar programme for pure speed might involve doing 10 x 100-metre sprints on a slight incline, again using the time it takes to walk back down as the recovery period. Those not used to training for speed in this all-out way should spend at least a month doing the following sort of programme: instead of going flat out on each sprint, start by running the first at about 50 per cent of full speed, increasing in 10 per cent increments so that you do not try to go flat out until the sixth dash. Do two more flat out and finish off with one at about 75 per cent and finally one again at 50 per cent.

Effective training for speed invariably requires at least one partner; running against the clock alone is extremely difficult even for specialist runners. In fact, a group of training partners is the best option as a friendly competitive spirit develops that helps everyone to go faster. Partners can also help with specialist drills for increasing speed such as sprinting in a harness. Sprinting against such resistance is a good way to develop explosive speed. In the absence of a proper athlete's harness, get a partner to loop a belt or a towel around your waist and hold you back as you try to sprint. Get him to vary the amount of resistance he gives you and exaggerate the high knee lift and the pumping of the arms, doing 6 sets over 50 yards. Throw some downhill sprints into your training occasionally, again in sets, and you should see a marked improvement fairly quickly.

Interval training can be usefully undertaken in the gym, too. Karateka, kickboxers and taekwondo exponents often work out using the punch bag, pads and speedball to build speed power and endurance. For a beginner working on a punch bag a simple routine provides a relatively severe training effect. If the trainee punches the bag continuously for a minute, using both hands, pulling the elbows right back as he makes each strike, and hits the bag as many times as he possibly can – aiming to do, say, 120 punches – the training effect is shattering. It is the same kind of effort an athlete has to make in sprinting 400 metres. Repeating for 3–5 sets develops excellent power and local muscular endurance in the arms, shoulders, torso and legs. It can be made even harder by doing a pattering action, only lightly touching the bag rather than actually hitting it with power, keeping the arms relaxed and not locking at the elbows, but still working at the fastest rate possible. Bag pattering is frustrating, but has a neuromuscular effect, allowing the trainee to make more rapid muscular contractions than would otherwise be possible.

Fig 9   For high kicks the bag needs to be hung high.

Figs 10–12   Frank Massar demonstrates a spinning reverse crescent kick on the heavy bag.

Fig 11

Fig 12

Figs 13–14   Doubling up on the kickboxer's
bag. A shin kick to the midsection is followed
up immediately with a roundhouse to the neck.

Fig 14

23

Figs 15–18   Using focus pads to practise the chop or axe kick.

Fig 16

Fig 17

24

Fig 18

Figs 19–20 Reverse punch with the right hand followed up by a roundhouse kick off the left leg. Note correct pad positioning for this sequence.

Fig 20

Fig 21   Master Kwang Jo Choi, 9th degree black belt in taekwondo, demonstrates a jumping back kick on the kick shield.

Fig 23

Figs 22–3   Training back kick on the focus pads.

Figs 24–8   Focus pads are excellent for developing good follow-through on techniques such as the push kick.

Fig 25

Fig 27

Fig 26

Fig 28

Obviously the bag routine can be varied to include kicks as well as punches for more advanced students, or even used exclusively for kicks. Groin kicks to the bottom of the bag or roundhouse kicks to the sides can be gruelling. Combinations of, for instance, roundhouse or turning kick and reverse punch can be practised in the same way, moving in and out as you attack and retreat. This can be done in sets, gradually increasing the speed and power of the kicks and punches. To practise repetition kicks in the pattering fashion requires a very high level of fitness and technique to be practical. In fact it is difficult to imagine a much more demanding routine than patter kicking a bag.

Doing rounds on focus pads is another highly-recommended form of interval training. Special pads are available for punching

Figs 29–30   Using two focus pads to receive a roundhouse shin kick, Muay Thai style.

Fig 30

and different kinds of kicks, ranging from small target pads for developing speed and accuracy to big padded kick shields for landing full-power thrusting and spinning kicks. The flat surface of the kick shield makes it preferable to the bag for doing kicks, since there is a danger of skimming off the bag if delivery is not perfect on techniques like side kick and back kick. Focus pads are extremely arduous, especially if the coach demands full commitment with every punch and kick. Maximum efforts quickly exhaust the athlete, but the good coach can raise his level of motivation with some well-chosen words. Calling out the shots and making the trainee think on his feet adds a touch of realism to the exercise and makes it more interesting.

Judoka and wrestlers can apply the same principles to their mat work, performing repetition skill drills with specific goals such as strength or speed increase. In judo, uchikomi is often used in this way. Uchikomi is repetitive practice of the entry for a particular throw without the actual completion being performed, and is an excellent way of developing head, hand and foot co-ordination

and in particular fast footwork, to enable the thrower to get in quickly for a technique. Wrestlers do the same type of practice and call it drilling. Sometimes the practice is done slowly with attention to detail in order to achieve biomechanical effectiveness. Beginners normally do sets of 10–20 repetitions, throwing on the last movement. This is by no means hard and fast, though. Sometimes, when doing interval training for speed, the class has to do as many repetitions as possible in a minute, then 45 seconds, then 30 seconds, then 15, then 5 and so on. It is interesting to observe how inexperienced people actually tighten up and go slower as they consciously try to go faster, while the experts seem to flow into their techniques in a relaxed yet dynamic fashion. This kind of speed training should be followed up with repetition throwing, or at the very least 5 sets of 5 turn ins, throwing on the fifth.

Nage komi, repetition throwing where the technique is completed every time, is arduous for the person being thrown as well as for the thrower. One way of making things less painful is to use a crash mat, which softens the fall considerably and allows the thrower to use full power and completely commit his body weight to each throw. The number of people training in a particular club determines how the nage komi is conducted. In some small clubs one person stands in front of a crash mat and goes through the line of everyone in the class. When he has thrown everyone the next player takes the line and so on until everyone has had a go. In larger classes this is not really practical and nage komi is done in groups of four, one person throwing each of the other three in the group 5 times. Without crash mats nage komi is best done in sets of 5, which prevents the person being thrown getting too badly battered. If more clubs had proper sprung floors, this would be a more popular form of training and players would be much more willing to take falls.

A groundwork counterpart to repetition

throwing is practising turn overs, which are popular drills in many wrestling clubs also. Judo players can run through armlocks, strangles and hold downs, as well as doing holding and escaping, where the person holding uses only 50 per cent power, allowing his partner to escape, at least initially, then progressively building up to 100 per cent.

In taekwondo and karate clubs pre-arranged sparring can have the same sort of effect as interval training, simply by raising the intensity of the attack and defence to full contest speed, the attacker and the defender alternating.

Swimming can duplicate all the conditions of interval training on the track. One very good way to get a training effect is to alternate strokes as described on page 20. The key point is to swim the flat-out lengths using your most effective stroke. Alternating between front crawl, back-stroke and breast-stroke can be particularly arduous, giving most of the muscles in the body a very comprehensive workout and providing a strong stimulus for both the aerobic and anaerobic energy systems. The butterfly, too, is obviously fine exercise, but is generally the province of the serious swimmer. Heavyweights in particular can benefit from swimming since their joints receive considerable shocks when attempting high intensity work on the track. Swimming tends to give the trainee a healthy appetite, whereas running quite often has the opposite effect (which is why it is the best effective aid to losing weight).

The variety of stroke can reduce the monotony element considerably. A good routine is to do a length breast-stroke at about 70 per cent of maximum, a length front crawl at 90–100 per cent, and then a recovery length swimming back-stroke at 50 per cent to get the breathing back under control. Try swapping the strokes around so that in one session you swim front crawl flat out, the next back-stroke and in the next breast-stroke, and you should see your overall speeds improve along with your basic heart-lung fitness.

VISUALISATION

Visualisation is a psychological technique employed by many top fighters and athletes. Basically it involves mentally rehearsing your performances, in the gym, on the track or in competition. Whether your goal is to run faster, hit harder or even to be invincible, you have to picture it and rehearse mentally. Some people visualise and rehearse victory in contest over their opponents dozens of times before the actual event, trying out different strategies and attacks, countering and dealing with counters, putting together combinations, getting out of trouble, imagining all the possible situations of the contest. Far from being mere fantasy, this technique has been proven to be effective and is well worth trying.

4 Flexibility

Flexibility, or suppleness, is one of the most important components of overall fitness, whatever your chosen sport. Some activities, such as karate, aikido and taekwondo, recognise this and train systematically to increase flexibility. Others, notably judo, boxing and wrestling, often tend to neglect flexibility as an aspect of conditioning, although of course this depends largely upon the priorities of individual instructors. It is important to remember that flexibility is a reversible component of fitness. Just as your gross muscular strength diminishes if you stop weight training, or your endurance decreases if you reduce your aerobic conditioning training, so too does your suppleness if you stop stretching. Curiously, people find this difficult to accept, believing themselves to be naturally flexible, strong or skilful, unaware of the extent to which these qualities are the result of training. They leave off weight training for months and go back expecting to match personal bests that were only established after months and sometimes years of arduous training sessions. This is a sure formula for disaster and is equally likely to lead to injury if applied to stretching.

As far as maintaining fitness for martial arts is concerned, if you are unable to train as regularly or as often as you would like, if you do nothing else, *stretch*. The reasons for and benefits of stretching are numerous and include enhanced athletic performance and reduced risk of injury. Once you become flexible it is a lot easier to maintain the condition than to regain it. Remember, consistency is the key, regular small doses are much better than isolated, frenzied sessions.

Karateka need to be flexible in order to function at high speed, and to have sufficient extension to reach the target in performing

Fig 31 Agea of Spain warms up before contest with a few head-height roundhouse kicks. Note the hip flexion, balance and concentration.

head height kicks, for instance. Judoka need to be able to bend low to get underneath their opponents when doing throws and to twist and wriggle in and out of groundwork situations. Flexible legs are vital in successfully defending against uchimata and so on, but very few judo players train systematically to improve their flexibility which is an error as much of the other training they do tends to make them tight. Wrestlers, too, tend to fall into this category, the chief exception being Japan's immense sumo wrestlers who combine massive bulk with remarkable

Fig 32   One of the benefits of being flexible: the ability to connect with a head-height kick in contest.

suppleness, but this flexibility is only achieved after years of brutal and exhausting training. The rikishi (sumo fighters) dedicate their lives to sumo in a system with rigid discipline; they are professional athletes, not keen amateurs. There is a big difference.

Among the most flexible of all fighters are taekwondo practitioners. The particular rule structure of taekwondo has led to the evolution of unique kicking techniques which have in turn required increasingly greater flexibility from practitioners. In terms of hamstring and hip flexibility they are unsurpassed by any other martial artists. Anyone aiming to improve their suppleness should give stretching exercises the kind of priority they deserve in training sessions. The information in this chapter is intended for all martial artists and combat sport practitioners, and anybody who wants to improve flexibility.

FACTORS AFFECTING FLEXIBILITY

1.   *Bone structure*   This is effectively predetermined for many who come to the martial arts as adults and imposes certain limits on achievable ranges of movement for the different parts of the body. The average man taking up karate at the age of 30 is unlikely ever to do the full box splits. Children have the potential for extreme ranges of movement and the younger they start training the greater their flexibility potential, but as in all training of youngsters there are obvious hazards and care should be taken to ensure they do not overdo it as injury may result.

2.   *Results of injury/trauma*   Old injuries freqently impair the individual's range of movement, joint mobility being particularly likely to suffer and most difficult to restore to full range of movement.

3.   *Joint capsules*   Some joints, notably the knee, contain cartilaginous structures which help to reduce friction and absorb shock. Stretching these can cause a loss of stability in the joint which may weaken it as a result and increases the likelihood of injury.

4.   *Muscle bulk*   Muscular size gained purely for show (i.e. body-building) can impair flexibility. Any body-building routine undertaken by martial artists and judoka should take this into consideration; prevention is easier than cure.

5.   *Fat deposits, bodyweight*   Overweight is a contributing factor to a lack of mobility in many cases, but just as with muscular bulk, it does not have to be. Sumo wrestlers routinely perform box splits and touch their foreheads to the floor while doing so. The average fat person will find, though, that rolls of blubber around the mid-section make some stretching exercises uncomfortable and breathing difficult, if not impossible.

6.   *Tendons*   These are non-elastic and, unlike muscles, are not designed to stretch, since their function is to provide stable attachments to the bones.

Fig 33　Hip flexibility is vital to good performance of techniques like yoko geri, the side kick.

WHEN TO STRETCH

Many martial artists would assert that stretching should be done every day, but steady improvement can be made by doing 3 sessions a week on alternate days. The time of day is not too important and stretching exercises can be fitted in anywhere, but ideally early morning is best. Remember that when you first wake up most of the blood is in the organs not the muscles, so you never feel as supple as later in the day. The temperature of the room, the time of day and your own state of tiredness or relaxation all affect how quickly and well you can stretch. Do not attempt maximum range of movement when cold. There can be a 20 per cent increase in mobility if the ambient temperature is over 43 degrees Celsius. A correspondingly dramatic decrease occurs in temperatures below 18 degrees Celsius. So in cold weather, or cold dojos, warm up gradually. There is an argument which says that for self-defence purposes you will not have time to warm up and need to be able to go 100 per cent at any given moment. This is a peculiarly specious notion, since in any life-threatening situation the body functions under the influence of adrenalin anyway. Also, self-defence techniques are rarely those which require big ranges of movement. If you choose to kick, for example, it is much more likely to be the groin or knee than the head that you aim for, so it is not an issue. Do not be in a hurry.

HOW TO STRETCH

A lot of scientific-sounding jargon is bandied about these days to describe stretch techniques. These are frequently terms coined by sports scientists and physiologists, describing their investigations into specific phenomena. Unfortunately, different researchers tend to invent their own vocabulary in order to describe their observations, which can be confusing. Since the aim here is not to explain the biochemistry of stretching but rather correct stretching techniques and their application for the martial artist, for the purposes of clarity only four labels will be used for four distinct methods of stretching. These are slow stretch, dynamic stretch, isometric stretch, and static stretch.

Slow stretch is very much in vogue with exercisers these days. Aerobics classes usually have a fair amount of it, but yoga is the epitome of this method. It is the basis of any stretch routine and should always be the first type of stretch to be undertaken in most circumstances. The muscle being stretched is slowly extended to the point where the stretch can be felt pulling on the muscle group, held for a few seconds, then relaxed, then returned to the stretched position, gradually increasing the range of movement each time until the fullest stretch possible is reached.

Dynamic stretching is a method of increasing flexibility by using ballistic motion to stretch the muscle and is frequently criticised as potentially dangerous by slow stretch advocates. The point is, though, that most martial artists need to be able to perform techniques at speed and in doing so are putting muscles and joints under exactly this kind of stress. An axe kick, for example, involves the mechanical action of swinging the leg above the head and bringing it down with force. This cannot be done slowly if it is to be effective, so the kicker has to practise the action at high speed. The risk of injury is only really strong if the kicker goes for maximum extension when cold, tired or stiff. Dynamic stretching requires a lot more care than slow stretching since the stresses involved are magnified; always start gently and build up to full range movements. There is a school of thought which argues that it demonstrates rather than develops flexibility. It can certainly help to maintain it. The correct way to prepare for practising the axe kick would be to do a complete slow stretch warm-up first and then begin leg swings, increasing the height until full range movements could comfortably be performed. Dynamic stretching is an integral part of taekwondo where head height combination kicking involving 360 degree rotations is standard.

Isometric stretching, or proprioceptive neuromuscular facilitation, to give it its high-tech name, is the most effective and severe form of flexibility training and if done correctly will give the quickest improvements. Isometric exercise sees force expressed without movement such as when a weight is held at arm's length, or the mid-point position in a press-up is maintained. Isometric stretching uses the same principle; unfortunately it is the hardest and most demanding way to stretch and should not be done more than 3 times a week on alternate days, although non-isometric stretching may be done on the 'rest days'. Isometric stretching involves putting the muscle group to be stretched in a stretched position then exerting maximal contractive force. The familiar exercise where you get a partner to kneel on one knee and put your foot on his shoulder and he then stands, raising the foot higher off the ground every couple of seconds until it is over head height, can be made much more effective by working isometrically. Instead of trying to get your head to your knee to feel the stretch, contract the muscles you are stretching forcefully, in this case the hamstrings, hold the contraction for 7 seconds then contract the antagonistic muscle group, in this case the quadriceps or thigh muscles. Go through this sequence 3 times and you will feel the difference. Build up the time until you are actually applying the contractive force throughout the stretch for up to a minute at a time. One problem with this kind of stretching is that you may experience chronic muscular soreness the following day, but gentle non-isometric stretching should ease this.

Static stretching is very demanding and involves putting the body into a stretched position by using sheer muscular control. Holding the leg up high off the ground, as in the position for a head-height front or side kick, is a form of this and requires considerable strength and muscular control as well as suppleness and the ability to relax those muscle groups which tend to impede such stretches. Holding the leg out at head height in the front kick position demands great strength in the thigh and abdominal muscles, very flexible hamstrings, and an awareness of how to relax them so that they do not prevent full extension of the limb.

The following is a simple all-body stretch routine which can take 20–30 minutes and may be done at any time, although early morning stretching, despite initial difficulties in getting warmed up, may be the most beneficial. A shortened version can usefully be performed before and after normal training sessions, perhaps 10 minutes to warm up and 10 minutes to finish off. This should be performed as an uninterrupted continuous routine. As you gain experience, do each exercise for as long as it takes for the stretch to feel effective, but initially try 5–10 repetitions of the movement, gradually trying to increase your range each time.

Fig 34   The bow, a yoga stretch for the front of the body.

Fig 35   Clasping the hands together behind the head maintains good shoulder girdle flexibility.

Fig 36　A position which simultaneously stretches both hips and shoulders.

Fig 37　Extreme flexibility is needed to reach positions like this one!

Fig 38　The sumo style squat, good for building leg strength and suppleness.

Figs 39–52   A variety of hip, groin and hamstring stretches.

Fig 40

Fig 41

Fig 42

Fig 43

Fig 44

Fig 45

Fig 47

Fig 46

Fig 48

Fig 49

Fig 50

Fig 51

Fig 52

Neck rolls
Shoulder circles and reach
Behind back clasps
Wrist circles
Side bends
Squat, then straighten legs, keeping hands touching floor
Straighten up and arch backwards, hands over head
Press-up position: alternate leg lunges (slow at first building up to rapid fluid movements)
Bow or cobra
Bow or cobra with open legs
Stand up, legs astride, alternate toe touching; bending at the waist, keeping legs straight and as wide apart as possible reach forwards, sideways and back through the legs. Legs still in the astride position, touch the floor with the elbows
Lunge position to the front to stretch groin, bend the front knee, keep the back leg straight, weight on front foot and ball of back foot
Squat down on the right foot keeping the left leg straight and repeat on the other side
Sit, legs astride, toe touching, head to knees and touch floor between legs

Fold legs in front of body, soles of feet touching, and push down knees to floor. Grasp ankles and bring forehead to touch feet
Sit down, legs straight out in front, and take hold of your feet, pulling the heels off the ground, stretching the calf muscles. Then touch your forehead on your knees
Hurdler's stretch and lie back
Front splits
Side or box splits
Crab

That completes the combination of stretching movements which should have you flexible and ready for more intense training. If purely concerned to stretch to increase flexibility (i.e. not going into a full practice session after completing the above) repeat the exercises, holding the stretched positions for one minute at a time. This latter method is particularly good for getting rid of soreness and stiffness from weight training, for example, but is not recommended where injured muscle groups are concerned.

5 Callisthenics

One of the best alternatives to weight training for the development of strength, speed and power is free exercise or callisthenics, which involve using the bodyweight for resistance and have the great advantage of requiring little or no expensive equipment. The effectiveness of such training is undisputed and many combat sports include callisthenics in their warm-up and conditioning routines, typically using lots of press-ups and sit-ups to build muscle tone and stamina. Mike Tyson claims never to have used weight training, declaring his formidable physique to be the product of sparring, roadwork and callisthenics. Such exercises are simple to do but must be undertaken gradually at first, allowing the joints time to get accustomed to the shock loading which is a feature of exercises like bunny hops and squat jumps. The bunny hop in particular has to be approached carefully and is not recommended for anyone who has had knee injuries or is overweight. Like weight training, circuits using these exercises can be devised for a variety of purposes.

The following is a form of aerobic circuit training which uses bodyweight and a minimum of equipment.

Raise heart rate by doing 10-minute blocks on exercise bike, skipping and running machine. Total: 30 minutes. Followed by:

3 × 30 press-ups
3 × 30 sit-ups
3 × 30 squat jumps

3 × 30 chins (assisted if necessary)
3 × 30 V sit-ups or crunches
3 × 30 lateral jumps

3 × 30 dips
3 × 30 leg raises
3 × 30 step-ups (30 each leg)

The trainee does 30 press-ups, rests for 30 seconds, does another 30 press-ups, rests for 30 seconds, then does a final 30 before moving on to the next exercise, and so on until the circuit is completed. Note that the circuit in this form is suitable only for very advanced trainees already possessing relatively high levels of fitness, and is structured so as to stress the whole body. Each group of 3 exercises hits 3 specific body areas, namely the upper body, mid-section and legs, in that order. Ray Stevens, the 1986 Commonwealth Judo Champion, used to do this circuit on alternate days, weight training in between. An indication of the remarkable strength and fitness it helped him to develop is that he could bench press 135kg (300lb) at a bodyweight of 85kg (13st) and run a half marathon in 1 hour 10 minutes.

This circuit is ideal for two people training together since one partner can work while the other rests, perhaps counting the reps if this proves helpful. A modified version for intermediate fighters might be:

Pre-circuit warm up: 7-minute blocks on exercise bike, skipping and running machine (the order may be varied according to taste). Total: 21 minutes. Followed by:

Press-ups: 10, 15, 20
Sit-ups: 10, 15, 20
Burpees: 10, 15, 20

Horizontal chins, done with the feet supported by a partner, or with the feet on the floor, lying prone and pulling up on a bar held by a partner: 10, 15, 20
Crunches: 10, 15, 20
Astride jumps: 10, 15, 20

Bench dips: 10, 15, 20
Leg raises: 10, 15, 20
Step-ups: 20, 25, 30 (each leg)

The beginner should modify the circuit still further, doing skipping, exercise bike and jogging machine for 4 minutes each prior to doing the above exercises in sets of 10. Using the principle of progressive resistance, the number of reps could then be gradually built up over a period of time, although of course overload could also be applied by reducing rest times to 20 seconds, or increasing the number of sets per exercise from 3 to 4, or any combination of these factors. One way to improve would be to add one rep per set per session, adding one minute to pre-circuit warm-up exercises per week. There are numerous permutations possible allowing the workload to be tailored to the trainee's current fitness level.

A simple exercise routine which requires no equipment is the 'Ten to One' set. The trainee selects 3 exercises, say press-ups, bent leg sit-ups and burpees. He starts by doing 10 of each, then 9 of each, then 8, and so on until he does one of each to finish. This amounts to a total of 55 reps of each exercise. The routine can be done as a warm-up, as a method of finishing off a session, or even while watching television. Doing declining sets makes it psychologically easier to finish and people tend to develop a faster rhythm towards the end. It can also be done in competition with a partner, although once it becomes a race, the quality of the exercises tends to deteriorate.

A host of special exercises have been devised by trainers looking for ways to add interest and variety to the training session:

Kneeling sit-ups
Sit-up and punch
Squat and kick
Burpee and kick/punch
Wrestler's bridge

Partner training:
Bridge pull-over holding partner's ankles
Resistance leg raises/sides
Overs and unders
Leg scissor sit-ups
Horse sit-ups (for neck of supporter)
Donkey raises
Squats with partner sitting on hips
Pull-ups

The physiology of callisthenics would seem to be different to that of weight training. The nature of such exercise tends to be low intensity and invites high repetition. Those who advocate callisthenics claim it is just like jogging or running: if you pace yourself and build up over a long period, you can go on for longer and longer. Indian wrestlers traditionally performed huge numbers of repetitions of exercises such as the baithak (a form of squat) and the dand (a kind of modified press-up or cat dip), frequently reaching the thousands. The weight-training advocate argues that the same results can be achieved in a shorter time with considerably less monotony by using heavy weights, because of the condensed nature of the work done. Different people, it seems, thrive on different kinds of exercise. While Mike Tyson never uses weights in training, Frank Bruno never feels prepared for a fight without them. Daley Thomson, probably the best decathlete of all times, tried weight training on occasion to improve his performance, but found he preferred to train for the same ends by doing repetition jumping (plyometrics) such as squat jumping over hurdles instead of squats with weights, for example. Personal preference is an important element of training sometimes described as the instinctive principle: doing what feels right for you, listening to your body, and adapting your training needs as necessary.

American footballer Herschel Walker, who reputedly has only 1.5 per cent body fat at a weight of 100 kg (15½ st) attributes his physique to free exercise. He was a flabby high school kid with good genetic potential, who was told by the school football coach to do press-ups and sit ups every time a commercial break occurred when he was watching television – something he tended to do too much. Just how much becomes apparent when you consider that currently he starts the day with a training session comprising 3,500 of each, normally in sets of 500, albeit now without the TV. The professional football club that employs him does not insist that he weight train like all other team members, recognising the highly disciplined nature and effectiveness of his training regimen.

6   Grappling Fit

Grappling or wrestling, pitting strength, determination, speed and skill against an opponent, is an excellent way to get fit. Types of grappling range from judo to wrestling, and practitioners of these sports require very high levels of fitness and muscular strength.

JUDO

Judo was founded by Doctor Jigoro Kano towards the end of the nineteenth century. The original concept was that of shugyo, an ex-

Fig 53   Beauty among the beasts: Ingrid Bergmahns of Belgium, 5 times World judo champion and Olympic gold medallist at light heavyweight.

tremely severe self-imposed discipline, ascetic by modern standards, through which the trainee developed an iron-willed determination to succeed in whatever he put his mind to. Training was the way to forge the spirit and to develop mental power and intelligence, in order to deal with the problems of existence. For the original judoka, judo was a way of life, not merely a sport. The trainees studied, analysed and developed techniques but were never enslaved by the concept as many of today's young sportsmen seem to be. The rules were much less complicated and limiting; basically, anything was allowed in randori (free play) that was not calculated to injure one's training partners. Ultimately the goal was not just a win on the mat, but self-realisation.

Judo has evolved into a modern Olympic combat sport, something which traditionalists see as having contributed to its deterioration. The pursuit of gold medals makes it a highly competitive, elitist activity, and at the highest level there is room only for the most superb athletes, many of whom now want to reap financial rewards for their performance and dedication, inevitably comparing themselves with other professional sportsmen. This attitude demeans the original scope of Kano's vision, which had a much broader aim than material gratification. A return to the roots, however, seems most unlikely.

The newcomer to judo is likely to find himself in a club where the emphasis is on training for competition, simply because that is what people enjoy most – the randori, trying to throw a resisting opponent who is trying to throw you – but this is rather like reducing a game of football to a penalty-taking contest. There is a lot more to judo than meets the eye.

Fig 54   Fierce abandonment and a willingness to take risks are the hallmarks of top flight international judo bouts.

It is a physically very demanding activity, something the general public probably only realised when they saw Brian Jacks demonstrate on the TV programme, *Superstars*, the remarkable combination of athletic abilities that had kept him at the top in judo for so long. He became European Superstars Champion, beating top sportsmen from a variety of other activities in the process.

It is no coincidence that beginners look unfit in judo – they are, and the strenuous nature of the activity finds it out. The judo player needs strength, agility, speed and stamina. One of the reasons it is so demanding is that fighters suffer from restricted oxygen intake as a result of being bent over and unable to breathe freely for large parts of the training and contest. The relatively fit person new to judo soon becomes aware of deficiencies in his forearms, lower back and neck as a result

of gripping and being pulled around. The novice who has done no other type of sport or foundation training will inevitably suffer chronic muscle stiffness for days after the first session. Many clubs run beginners' courses for just this reason, to prepare the novice for his first 'real' session.

The beginner invariably discovers that the first problem is grip strength. The forearms pump up and it becomes impossible to move the fingers after a few minutes of maximum effort in a grading or kyu grade competition. This is due to the build-up of lactic acid in the muscles. Regular training in either the strength endurance circuit using weights (*see* Chapter 9) or specialist grip exercises take care of this.

Perhaps more than in any other sport, the judo player needs a complete balance of physical qualities and must develop his

Fig 55   The ippon throw, the goal of training in sport judo.

Fig 56   Agility and fast footwork are major components of skilful judo.

speed, strength, skill, stamina and suppleness in harmony. There have been many British judo fighters renowned for their fitness, including Brian Jacks, Dave Starbrook and more recently Neil Adams, all of them at their peak a match for just about anyone in the world. Training methods and preferences among the top fighters differ considerably, but the common factors are extremely hard work coupled with consistency both on and off the mat. Dave Starbrook was perhaps the best example of sheer force of will overcoming limiting factors. He was so lacking in suppleness he could not touch his toes yet he developed fantastic strength and stamina and one of the fastest, most unstoppable tai-otoshis ever seen. He went on to win Olympic silver and bronze, as well as two world bronze medals. It has always been a characteristic of judo, that the impossible can be achieved through will and dedication.

The lighter weight category judo fighters tend to have the most efficient builds, and the

49

nature of lightweight judo calls for the ability to work at a very high energy output continuously throughout a contest. Lightweight action tends to be non-stop, and pound for pound these fighters are among the fittest and strongest of athletes. One of the most highly trained of lightweights was Japan's Katsuhiko Kashiwazaki, who came to live in London for a year after retiring having won the World Under 65kg title in 1981 in Maastricht, Holland. He was a remarkable example of will coupled with dedication.

While in London, Kashiwazaki was chief instructor at the Budokwai judo club and continued to train much as he had when he was still a competitor. I was fortunate to belong to a group of about half a dozen who were able to train with him outside the dojo. Kashiwazaki was very unusual in that he had reached the pinnacle of his chosen sport while working full-time as a high school teacher in Japan in an age when most top competitors are effectively professionals training full-time. His training philosophy went along the lines that 'the race is not to the swift nor to the strong, but to the one who endures'.

The first session, at eight o'clock one Monday morning, comprised a 3-mile run which took about 20 minutes, then a period of sprinting up and down the terraces at Crystal Palace National Sports Centre. We had to sprint up the steps in pairs, and jog back down. We ran up first touching every step, then every second step, then every third step. We then had to do it with a training partner of similar weight on our backs. I weighed 98 kg (15½ st) at the time and had to carry Jim Webb, who was even heavier. I felt nauseous and my legs wobbled even though I could breathe without much difficulty. I vomited twice, despite having not eaten. Kashiwazaki suggested that if my legs were really tired and would not stop trembling – a common phenomenon he described as 'laughing legs' – I should go up the steps wheelbarrow-fashion on my hands, which I did. I thought that I had never trained

so hard before, but after a couple of weeks I realised that the training, while very hard, was not impossible. Kashiwazaki was quick to stress this. 'Anyone can do my training once or twice, even for a couple of weeks, but the really important thing is to train every day, that is not so easy. I did this every day for ten years before I became world champion.'

Something that became clear despite the way training varied from day to day was that variety and consistency are really opposite sides of the same coin. His approach was relatively uncomplicated; recognising that everyone must work for a living, training lasted for 1½ hours in the morning before work, and involved running, callisthenics, stretching, shadow uchikomi and randori. Five nights a week we did judo every evening for 1½–2 hours. Those who were training to get their weight down sometimes ran before going to bed. All of us achieved some of our best results as a direct consequence of this training. I myself won a silver medal in the All England Championships and then cut my weight down to 85kg (13½st).

Training Fitness and Skill Together

Nage komi, or repetition throwing, is an extremely arduous form of fitness training for both the thrower and the person or persons being thrown. It has the added advantage of being an excellent way to develop skill. The technique chosen, too, has an important bearing on the exercise effect which results. De ashi-barai, which is essentially a timing-based throw, will require a lot less energy expenditure than tai-otoshi or ippon seoi-nage. The exercise becomes more or less difficult depending on how much effort the thrower puts into each individual technique. There is an analogy with hitting a punch bag: if you pace yourself and place your punches you will use a lot less energy than if you hit it as hard and fast as you possibly can.

Throwing skills need to be fast and sharp, though, and are best practised early in the training session while you are still fresh, or at the end, when although weary you will be thoroughly warmed up and relaxed as well as able to focus on particular problems you may have experienced with certain individuals or physical types. In an ideal world, throwing skills might best be practised in a separate session. In any event they are best practised in conjunction with uchikomi, helping to make the latter more meaningful and realistic. Concentration is very important; there is absolutely no point in switching off mentally and going through the motions as if you were doing a jog.

Every repetition you make should be vitally alive and you should be getting feedback from the experience. Ask partners how techniques feel. Sometimes if you concentrate only on how *you* feel, you can be misled. It is not so important, particularly in uchikomi, that a technique or throwing position feels powerful to you; your partner has to feel it could be effective. If you make a turn in or attack and he feels completely stable and on balance, there is something lacking in your technique. If you are in position for tai-otoshi, say, thinking, 'This is a strong position' and he is thinking exactly the same about his defence, your throw is unlikely to be effective when you try it in randori or contest.

Another important consideration is that when you come to fight in contest you will have a lot more space than you normally have in randori. In the relatively controlled nage komi situation you should try to cover ground and use as much space as possible, as this allows maximum force to be transmitted into the throwing action. Too often in this country, where dojos tend to be a lot smaller than in Japan, people try almost to throw 'on the spot' as it were, and while there are obviously some advantages to this it is also important to make use of space when it is available.

In nage komi and randori aim to create a state of confusion so that you can perform a throw with the kind of suddenness that makes it so effective in contest. Throwing skills are not robotic and should not be practised sloppily. Try to make every throw like a knock-out punch – if you do it properly your partner should feel as though he's been hit by a bolt from the blue!

Take-downs into ne-waza should be practised regularly, and make a good way to start off a ne-waza training session. Holding and escaping should also be practised with partners co-operating, trying 50, 60, 70, 80, 90 and 100 per cent both to escape and to keep the hold on.

Standard model for judo training session:
10 minutes stretching and warming-up
10 minutes instruction on technical points
20 minues uchikomi and nage komi
40 minutes randori
20 minutes ne-waza
10 minutes warming-down and stretching

The randori can be divided into various lengths, possibilities include 8×5 minute practices, 7×6, 10×4, or 13×3, or any combination of varying lengths, with the intention of getting the players to train at variable pace. If you are used to training for 6 minutes a practice it takes some time to adjust to suddenly having only half that time in which to weigh up and deal with an opponent. Normally it is helpful to students if the instructor indicates how the randori is to be broken up at the beginning. To avoid the risk of collisions and injuries in a crowded dojo, the instructor might split the class into two either by experience or by weight, and have half on the mat doing randori while the other half does uchikomi around the edges of the mat. This can be particularly useful prior to a big competition, helping trainees to get used to the gaps which occur between contests. It should not be the norm when training for half the class to stand around while the others work. It is better to train continuously.

WRESTLING

Wrestling is probably the oldest of the combat sports and in earlier times it was certainly the most widespread. Almost every culture since the beginning of time has enjoyed some form of wrestling, and many local and regional forms continue to thrive apart from the Olympic movement. Some of these are highly specialised. They include wrestling from a grip on the opponent's belt, as in Finnish glima and the lucha canaria of Tenerife, to jacket wrestling like Russian sombo (previously known as sambo), which closely resembles judo in many respects. There are also the 'naked' varieties ranging from Cumberland and Westmorland, where fighters adopt a grip with arms around each other and hands clasped before starting, to the village wrestling practised in earth pits in India, to Turkish oil wrestling, where the contestants oil up to make obtaining a grip even more difficult.

As a spectator sport, wrestling suffers by comparison with all-action boxing or taekwondo, largely because evenly-matched opponents tend to negate one another, giving the impression to the untrained eye that nothing is happening. However, although one of the least glamorous combat sports, wrestling is one of the most demanding and top wrestlers are among the fittest athletes anywhere. The sport demands a very high physial work capacity, good balance, great strength, stamina, speed, agility and determination. Wrestling is an Olympic sport in its own right now, and it is important to distinguish between the acrobatic pantomimes described as 'professional wrestling' which often appear on television, and the real sport. Probably the only professional wrestling which is not pure showmanship is Japanese sumo. As a spectator sport it is undeniably entertaining even to the uninitiated, especially when the endless rituals and pauses between bouts are edited out by television.

The dohyo is the domain of Japan's giant athletes, selected from an early age because of genetic potential for size and power. Sumo is a tradition-laden activity and many of the training methods the heya (sumo stables) use are unique. The rikishi are renowned for both strength and suppleness.

The Olympic sport consists of two distinct types of wrestling, Graeco-Roman and Freestyle. Basically, the Graeco-Roman style allows only grips and holds above the waist, whereas in Freestyle leg grabs and the like are also allowed. As with most of the other combat sports a strong neck is vitally important. The wrestler concedes a score if he is passive, or if his shoulders touch the mat for even a few seconds, and he must be able to twist and turn, sometimes with the combined weight of two bodies plus the opposing muscle power of the other wrestler on his neck. The modern amateur wrestler wears only a leotard and boots and aims to score points by taking down his opponent and pinning him to the mat. Skills are of necessity more limited and techniques less varied than in the jacket wrestling sports; only the body can be gripped. One consquence is that the wrestler is normally in even better physical condition than his counterparts in judo and sombo: where it is not possible to win through superior skills, physical condition can be the deciding factor. The passivity rules in the sport which instantly penalise any coasting in the course of a contest, also spur the wrestler to greater physical condition. Of course, at the highest level all fighters are athletes training as hard as possible, so there is not a lot in it as far as physical condition goes.

Traditionally wrestlers run, weight train, do callisthenics and mat work, practising basic skills and contesting with one another. Fighting normally begins from a standing position or off the floor with one wrestler on all fours and the other above and behind him, virtually on his back. The similarities with judo inevitably make the training requirements similar, the main difference being the wider skills and techniques that the jacket allows.

7 Striking Systems

KARATE

There is a clear dichotomy in the karate world between those who see themselves as martial artists and those who consider themselves to be sportsmen. Of all the martial arts, karate has the highest profile in the public consciousness, but the name, which simply means open or empty hand, is a blanket term which now describes a whole range of disparate activities. There are literally dozens of different styles of karate, and newcomers are often confused by this plethora of competing systems so outwardly similar, yet so fiercely independent of each other.

The history of modern karate tends to be described as beginning with Gichin Funakoshi. This is like saying that the history of America began with Columbus. It was Funakoshi who took karate from its home in Okinawa to the Japanese mainland, but it had existed on Okinawa for centuries before his birth. Where karate is predominantly Japanese in both forms and function, Funakoshi was Okinawan, a practitioner of Okinawa-te, an indigenous fighting system of the Ryukyu islands that probably owed much to various Chinese martial systems which had been absorbed in the islands over the years. A schoolmaster, Funakoshi was observed teaching karate by several high-ranking Japanese naval officers on a visit to the islands. He was invited to Tokyo to demonstrate his art to the Emperor himself, and his demonstration was so well received that he decided to remain in Japan and opened the first karate school in the country, the Shotokan.

The three principle karate styles in Okinawa were Shuri-te, Naha-te and Tomari-te, which emerged contemporaneously in different geographical regions. Funakoshi's Shotokan derived from the Shuri-te style but underwent many subtle alterations from the original form. The chief reason for this was the spread of clubs and instructors throughout the country. Students who reached high levels of competence opened their own dojos and began teaching, introducing their own personal idiosyncrasies, which ultimately led to the fragmentation of karate into the myriad styles, schools and associations existing today – hence the split between sports-orientated karaketa and the traditionalists for whom karate is a mental and physical discipline which the student practises in order to develop the ultimate, weaponless self-defence system and to perfect his character. Many techniques of the original karate were intentionally lethal, and the idea of sparring or free fighting, still less contest, was anathema to the traditional school of thought. Techniques such as straight-finger strikes to the eyes (nukite), open (shuto) handed strikes to the throat, elbow strikes (empi) to the temple and numerous others are too dangerous to allow contact and are very sensibly not allowed even in the so-called full contact versions of the sport. With ambitions to etablish karate as an Olympic sport running high, the dichotomy seems likely to become even more marked as time goes on, although unlike judo, traditional karate seems to be thriving alongside the sport forms.

The Modern Sport

Shotokan, Shotokai, Wado Ryu, Goju Ryu, Kyokushinkai, Shukokai, Shito Ryu and a host of other less well-organised and administered styles compete for new members in Britain today. It is therefore dangerous to use the term karate generically when talking about tailored fitness programmes. Style in karate may only mean the difference in the way a few techniques are performed in one school as compared to another, such as in the variants of the mawashi-geri or round-house kick and lengths of stances found in wado ryu and shotokan, but in some cases it can mean totally different ethical and philosophical attitudes and competition structure. The kind of fitness the karateka needs will be determined by the style of karate he wants to do. On a very simple level the chief differences revolve around the degree of physical contact allowed and the scoring systems that appertain.

Karate competition (excluding kata) is either semi-contact or full contact. The latter tends to be how practitioners of semi-contact styles refer to the kyokushinkai style founded by Masutatsu Oyama. Full contact is something of a misnomer since only certain techniques are allowed and many fundamental actions, such as the punch to the face/head area and the kick to the groin, are not allowed. The kyokushinkai fighters refer to their form of competition as knockdown karate, since one fighter's superiority over another is demonstrated by his ability to knock the other down, without resorting to illegal techniques. This type of karate requires a high degree of physical toughness, especially about the legs and abdomen. One of the hallmarks of the style is the thigh kick, which is delivered using the shin or instep to deaden the nerves in the opponent's thigh. Anyone who has ever had a 'dead leg' will know how disabling this can be. Kyokushinkai hold open competitions, but their predilection for thigh kicks makes them unpopular with exponents of other styles.

The different organisations and styles of karate have created their own systems of competition and there is a confusing variety of types of karate contest. Karate was originally a martial art intended for self-defence and was considered to be too dangerous for freestyle fighting to be allowed, with the res-

ult that karateka eager to make their training ever more realistic and to gauge their development tried harder and harder in their pre-arranged sparring, doing their series of attacks and defences in an increasingly realistic fashion. The top exponents consequently achieved such good control that it was possible to develop a more open-ended system, allowing competition which has evolved into a dynamic sport.

The sport karate fighter competing under World Union of Karate Organisations rules is not allowed to make heavy contact in competition. If he draws blood he is disqualified, if he makes contact with his opponent's head he is penalised, if he hits his opponents full power to the body he may be disqualified. Control and timing are the order of the day, and yet for a technique to score it has to be delivered with effective power. At international level an ineffectual attack or counter is invariably punished severely, so the fighter must have a clear idea of what is and what is not acceptable in terms of contact, which only comes from experience.

The sport karate fighter's chief prerequisites are speed and control. Of course he needs endurance to get through contest after contest, but if he has not got the speed needed to score the points he will never be a successful competitor. If he lacks control and draws blood he will be automatically disqualified; for that reason and even more importantly for the safety of his opponents, control is paramount. All good karate men are fast, and the fastest tend to be the champions. Speed is developed in the dojo through training in basic punching, kicking, blocking and sweeping techniques. Punches are of course quicker than kicks, but kicks are effective at a greater range as well as being more powerful and harder to block. High kicks to the head, while very spectacular, tend not to be used very often as the risk of being countered with a foot-sweep or short fast reverse punch is very high. A successful head-height kick in competition is

Fig 57 Karateka have to cover ground quickly and get in fast to score in contest.

normally the mark of a much superior fighter. Many fighters like to use a flurry of techniques, mounting combination attacks using both kicks and punches to pressure their opponents into making mistakes.

The karateka has to be able to bounce up and down on the balls of his feet throughout the course of a match, to present a constantly moving target to the opponent. This avoids being caught flat-footed or square and conceding ippon. A technique is never judged as effective if the fighter is moving away from it. The converse is also true, and the majority of ippons tend to come from gyaku-zuki counter punches as the opponents comes into attack. Skipping has an obvious application as it makes fighters light on their feet and develops the ability to change direction swiftly and to keep constantly on the move.

Within sport karate there are basically two

types of competition, shobu ippon and san-bon ippon. These terms describe a 1-point system and a 3-point system. The 1-point system was the original scoring mode for karate contests. Between two experts it was believed that the first blow to land would be lethal or at the very least would incapacitate the opponent. As a result, the early karate competitions were sudden death encounters, with the first man to make a mistake the loser, a situation which paralleled what might happen in a real-life situation. Unfortunately it proved to be unattractive to spectators since fighters were extremely careful and reluctant to open up in a situation where the first mistake would be the last. To make the activity more spectator-orientated, the waza-air or half-point was introduced for techniques which, while lacking the perfection of the ippon, were worthy of a score. This traditional form of competition is still held in some organisa-

Fig 58 Wayne Otto of England scores with a back kick on the way to the
European karate title in 1988.

Fig 59 Shotokan star George Best shows that
head-height kicks can be effective in karate.

tions, notably the extremely well run Karate Union of Great Britain which has a well-balanced approach to the disparate trends of modern and traditional karate.

Those groups belonging to WUKO have adopted the more spectator-orientated Sanbon shobu, which is a 3-ippon system that often sees a bout decided by 6 waza-ari scoring techniques, 2 waza-aris adding up to 1 ippon. This results in a very different kind of contest and a noticeable broadening of the skills displayed. A fighter can be losing by 5 waza-aris and still come back to win, something which is of course only possible if he is able to work out and exploit his opponent's weaknesses.

The knockdown karate fighter similarly needs speed to succeed but endurance and toughness are equally vital components of his fitness as he is likely to take considerable punishment to the body, which tends to sap both speed and strength. He needs to be well conditioned especially in the forearms, and also in the legs, which have to take the kind of punishment boxers and kickboxers suffer in their sports. As well as interval training on the track, aerobic gym circuits are recommended, weights-type as well as high-repetition callisthenics. Such additional conditioning for the abdomen and legs pays dividends. The real key to durability and toughness is a high level of cardiovascular fitness coupled with mental determination. One way to develop these is to fight a number of opponents one after the other. Even a much weaker fighter becomes a challenge when your strength has been sapped by dealing with a dozen before you get to him. The supreme example of this sort of training in the kyokushinkai style is the 100 kumite, where the high-level exponent fights a hundred opponents in knockdown style and must not be knocked down himself even once if he is to successfully complete it. Steve Arneil, 7th dan and head of kyokushinkai in Britain, is one of the few to have achieved this remarkable feat.

Kata

Kata training is the core curriculum for karate students. The kata are the forms of the art, which embody the knowledge and insight of past masters; they are extremely demanding sequences of movements strung together in a choreographed fashion in which the trainee practises a series of defences and counter-attacks against multiple assailants. There is an analogy with shadow-boxing except that the forms are rigidly set, the kata is always performed as the same sequence of movements. Repeatedly performing a single kata requires great concentration and is a well-established traditional way of improving basic technique. As with most things Japanese, repetition is considered the key to progress.

One aspect of karate conditioning which has not been dealt with is hand conditioning. The traditional Okinawan method was to pound the makiwara, a wooden post with a straw pad wrapped around it, until the knuckles bled. This would be continually repeated, never allowing the damage to heal completely, until huge calluses formed to protect the knuckles, resulting in an unsightly deformation of the hands. It is difficult to see the relevance of such training to the modern karate man; although there are some who see it as an intrinsic part of their development as serious karateka, sport karate champions tend to ignore it. Most trainees do press-ups on the knuckles, fingertips and wrists on a wooden floor to develop their hand and wrist strength.

Traditional Training Methods of Okinawan Te

The Okinawan systems of karate attached tremendous importance to the development of hand strength and evolved a variety of training mechanisms to achieve this. Before undertaking any of the hand strengthening exercises of the system the trainee was expected to master the horse stance (kibi-dachi in Japanese systems), a kind of wide-legged half squat, similar to that of the sumo wrestler, but not so deep and with the back kept straight. This basic stance was the foundation of the whole system, building strong, flexible legs and hips and balance. The trained exponent of te would commonly be required by his sensei to hold this stance for two hours or more at a time.

To develop hand and grip strength, primitive but effective weight-training equipment was evolved. The makiage gu is a kind of wrist roller, a rack with a revolving wooden bar from which a weight is hung by a rope. Twisting the bar to slowly raise and lower the weight develops the hands, wrists and forearms. Another more versatile device was the chikaraishi or power stone, which took

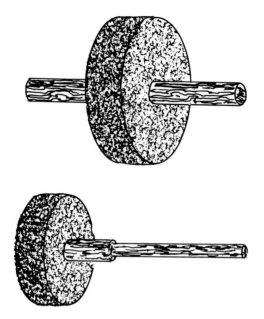

Fig 60   Power stones.

various forms but were basically primitive weights. Sometimes used like a swingbell, with the stone in the middle and the wood protruding from either end, the chikaraishi could be used to develop the muscles of the arms and shoulders. Alternatively, the stone weight would be at one end of the stick, like a hammer, and exercises were devised to develop mainly the shoulders, forearms and wrists.

A more interesting machine was a sort of makiwara with a weighted lever. Basically, this was a post wrapped in straw with a lever attached. The trainee gripped the lever with one hand, catching it as he would an opponent's wrist or jacket. Pulling on the lever, which would provide resistance because of the weight on the other end, he would then kick and strike the post with an open-handed blow.

Other methods of developing a strong grip were less elaborate and involved walking up and down the dojo in a particular stance grip-

ping the top rim of a jar which could be filled with sand, water, or even lead shot, depending upon the level of the student.

One of the most gruelling training drills was known as the penetrating hand, or Kanshu, derived from Chinese sources and sometimes known as the iron palm or hand. This involved filling a receptacle with powder or some other soft substance, and the trainee would practise driving his hand into it, using straight-fingered strikes. The material would be periodically changed to something harder, using rice, sand, beans, and finally pebbles, until the hands became fully conditioned. In Chinese systems the same process is followed but frequently different strikes are used, such as the palm heel or a back-handed blow.

TAEKWONDO

As with karate, taekwondo is divided into two broad groups, those who do semi-contact and those who do full contact. While certain elements remain common, the varying demands of the two activities tend to result in differences in emphasis in training. The semi-contact fighter fits in virtually the same category as the karateka, except that there is considerably more emphasis on high kicking techniques, often involving jumping and spinning. The full contact fighter's conditioning training has similarities with that of the kickboxer or knockdown karate fighter, although the legs are not a target area in taekwondo. Both versions of the sport require a high degree of fitness, the ability to keep moving and firing techniques. Perhaps the most important common components of fitness that they require are spring in the legs and flexibility. Agility, too, is obviously desirable since not getting hit can be every bit as important as hitting, whether semi or full contact.

Taekwondo has many elements in common with Japanese karate, which tends to

Fig 61   Jumping plays a large part in taekwondo training and competition.

Fig 62   Pin-point accuracy and control from Master Choi as he demonstrates a jumping twisting kick.

confuse people – some even refer to it as Korean karate – but really it is quite different, the full contact version in particular. The chief difference is in the emphasis given to kicking techniques. The rules are structured to encourage head-height kicks and the aim is to knock the opponent out with a kick. Punching attacks to the face are illegal, and the majority of punching attacks to the body are to set the opponent up for kicks. Because the back is not a scoring target area and sweeps are not allowed, a whole new range of spinning and jumping kicks have developed which require tremendous athleticism.

Training for Taekwondo

Normal training in taekwondo involves considerable jumping and bounding anyway, but there are some forms of plyometric training which are not commonly performed in

the dojang. These are mainly jumping exercises but come under the general heading of shock exercises, and are recommended for any combat sportsman or martial artist who wants to develop spring in his legs. They are, however, of a very intense nature and require considerable preconditioning of the leg muscles to minimise the risk of injury. Heavyweights in particular need to be careful in this area.

The depth jump is a plyometric exercise that has been used successfully by a number of power athletes including weight lifters and long and high jumpers. In its simplest form it involves jumping off a 1m (3ft) high bench into a squat and immediately leaping up and over another bench of a similar height. Those whose joints are unable to withstand the shock of such training can use a trampoline, although the training effect is somewhat diminished.

Running is an essential part of taekwondo fitness just as it is for karate and kickboxing. (*See* section on interval training, pp. 21–30). To build greater power and endurance a resistance harness can be employed – failing that, get a partner to loop a belt around you and run against it as he gives you resistance. Another alternative is to run with something – a tyre, an old mattress or even a judo mat – tied to your waist by a rope and dragging along the floor behind you.

Shuttle runs with hand-held weights are a very severe form of quality fitness work and can be done inside the dojo or on the sports field or track. Hill sprints build great reserves of stamina and leg strength and done as interval training pay dividends. Traditional athletics events such as the hurdles, the long and high jump are all valuable training for taekwondo. The reverse is also true: Olympic heptathlete Judy Simpson was a national taekwondo champion before opting to pursue a career in athletics.

The mid-section is also an area which can receive considerable punishment in a taekwondo tournament; like the legs, it too must be in good condition.

As well as traditional callisthenics, there are a few specialist exercises that are particularly useful for taekwondo exponents: the standard burpee modified to include a jumping front kick; squat thrusts without allowing the feet to touch the floor (kickbacks); skipping using a leather rope and splitting the feet forwards and sideways.

BOXING

Boxing, 'the noble art of self-defence', like wrestling, is a very old sport and was one of the original Olympic games in ancient Greece. Those same games also included the ultimate in combat sports, Pankratium, a kind of all-in fighting without weapons which frequently ended with one opponent or the other blinded, maimed or dead, and which was eventually removed from the list of events because of the high number of fatalities incurred.

Boxing, however, thrived and carried on down through the era of the Roman Empire, when it became afflicted by the same kind of decadence that tainted so much of Roman sport. The public, used to seeing life-and-death struggles enacted in the arena by armed gladiators, were not satisfied by the sight of two athletes simply punching one another, so the cestus was introduced, a vicious arrangement of leather straps and metal studs which was wrapped around the hand like the modern boxer's bandages, and greatly increased the likelihood of one fighter battering the other to death. Such was the appetite for brutality by the time of Caligula, boxers were actually chained to prevent them from moving and avoiding cestus-weighted punches, so the 'sport' was reduced to blow-for-blow bludgeoning which invariably ended in death.

Through the centuries the sport has developed, the fighters' skills have been refined, and rules for their protection have evolved, but it remains an inherently dangerous activity and deaths do still occasionally occur. The aim is to knock the opponent out, inflict sufficient damage to stop him carrying on with the contest, or outpoint him by landing more and better punches. The danger of damage – particularly to the eyes, nose and ears – is greater in boxing than in any other combat sport, and it grows proportionally greater the more tired the fighter becomes. Repeated blows to the head can also damage the brain; becoming 'punch drunk' is a real hazard for professionals, though an extremely unlikely occurrence in amateur boxing. Referees in amateur bouts never allow a fighter to suffer the kind of punishment sometimes inflicted in professional bouts. The element of danger which is intrinsic even to the amateur sport means that fighters must undergo a medical examination prior to fighting and be matched for weight.

Fitness for Kickboxing

Kickboxing is primarily an Asian sport, which has been imported because of a growing demand for realism in combat sports. Muay Thai, the indigenous fighting system in Thailand, is probably the hardest of all forms. The product of a Third World nation where life is cheap, fighting is a way out of poverty, a way to survive. At one time full contact was permitted to the head using bare elbow and knee strikes, but these blows have been restricted in an attempt to clean up the sport's image following a succession of deaths in the ring.

The kickboxer has the most demanding task of all in preparing himself for battle in the rope ring. As well as needing the speed and power of a karateka he has to be able to absorb punishment, too – the clinches so common in Western boxing where one fighter holds on to the other to get a rest are merely an opportunity to use knee strikes. The demands of ordinary boxing are gruelling enough – the boxer normally has the most specialised abdominal condition of any combat sportsman – but the kickboxer has also to be able to kick effectively and in some cases must condition the legs to receive kicks. The Muay Thai specialist has to deal with crippling leg kicking attacks, and physical toughness is possibly the main prerequisite of this sport.

The amateur kickboxer's training will involve circuits, roadwork, skipping, sparring and basic fitness routines similar to those used in preparing karateka and taekwondo fighters. Because of the full contact nature of the sport, however, other specialised training has to be done, such as chewing things like pieces of hose pipe to develop 'a strong chin', and exercises for the neck to increase

Fig 63   Kickboxers need to be in peak condition to withstand the brutal punishment routinely dealt out in the sport.

the ability to resist a punch. The emphasis in training will be on developing hand speed, which means intensive training on focus pads, also on developing punching power and kicking ability by using the heavy bag. The proper kickboxer's bag is a long, heavy cylinder of leather filled with horse hair and an internal sandbag which can be battered with the shins as well as the feet and hangs only a foot or so off the floor so the devastating low-level thigh kicks can be slammed in.

Shin kicking the bag is an important part of conditioning the shins for Thai boxing, but is less relevant to the American-style contact karate which takes place in a boxing ring, where contact below the waist is not permitted. Kyokushinkai is the only style of karate which permits low kicks to the legs and similar conditioning is undertaken by their members when preparing for contest. A popular demonstration of the power and effectiveness of such kicking involves breaking a baseball bat with a shin kick.

Callisthenics have always been preferred over weight training in kickboxing, and the successes of World Heavyweight Boxing Champion 'Iron' Mike Tyson, have reaffirmed their effectiveness. Tyson relies on routines consisting of press-ups, sit-ups, duck walking, squat thrusts and the like combined with pad work, speedball, heavy bag, skipping, roadwork and sparring to ensure that he is always in tip-top physical condition. Tyson's most remarkable attribute, though, is his psychological preparedness. His attitude in the ring epitomises the notion of killer instinct. He never lets his man off the hook once he is in trouble, always aiming to knock him out, rather than outpoint him. This is very much the professional attitude, in sharp contrast to that which prevails in amateur boxing, perhaps best exemplified by the top Russians, who even in the Olympic games invariably seek only to outpoint, rather than damage their opponents. The intention to damage is the great objection which is always made against professional boxing, and one of the reasons that it has declined in popularity as a sport practised in schools. Kickboxing is potentially even more brutal and it is difficult to see how the sport can hope to develop in an already hostile climate of opinion.

Many take up the training for boxing and kickboxing without ever getting in the ring and actually fighting in a match. Some do not even spar, but find that the training is a superb way to get and keep fit, to increase self-confidence, and to build character.

8 Weight Training

The Pros and Cons

Weight training is an extremely popular form of strength and conditioning training, and routines vary enormously according to the specific aims of the individual. Weights can be used for gaining or losing weight, depending upon the tailoring of training programmes and diet, which makes them doubly attractive to anyone wishing to change weight categories as well as modify his physical condition.

Perhaps the most useful advice for those embarking upon a weight-training programme is to learn the correct exercise technique, and to start light and build up gradually. This refers to frequency as well as intensity. Bearing in mind that any weight-training programmes undertaken will to some extent conflict with the sportsman's chosen activity, it is very important to get the balance of effort right. Whereas a bodybuilder or powerlifter may train very effectively doing 4 or 5 workouts a week with heavy weights, the karateka or judoka emulating such a plan will almost inevitably overtrain. Weights can be used with such frequency if the aim is weight control and endurance, but will of necessity be light-to-medium poundages. Where heavy weights are being handled on top of hard training of a combative nature, 2 sessions a week is probably ideal, 3 sessions maximum. As so often, more is not always better. Weight training can produce rapid improvements in speed, strength and stamina; it can also cause slipped discs and hernias if approached wrongly. The key to progress is correct exercise technique coupled with progressive resistance.

Weight training has proved to be a very versatile exercise system. The bodybuilder is concerned primarily with developing muscle mass while keeping bodyfat to a minimum; the Olympic weightlifter aims to develop the sheer power and athleticism necessary to hoist massive weights overhead in the clean and jerk or snatch. But training for such activities is in fact highly specialised even though it may seem very similar to the uninformed. Even powerlifting, where the maximum amount of sheer weight that can be shifted at a single attempt in bench press, squat or dead lift determines who wins, requires a modified training methodology to bodybuilding or weightlifting. How much more specialised, then, are the routines for combat sports as different as taekwondo and wrestling?

The fighter or martial artist actually falls into the most specialised category of weight trainer, that of the athlete or sportsman, who, whatever his field, has essentially the same goal: improved sports performance. However, the fighter is well advised to leave his ego at home when he goes weight training. Attempting to handle too much weight too soon, competing with specialist weightlifters and bodybuilders is courting disaster. For such athletes, weight training constitutes their entire workload; often they have been training for years specifically to lift heavier weights. Outside the gym their chief concern is to rest and recuperate, which is half the process. There is no point in putting your body through punishing workouts if you do not give it a chance to recover and replenish itself. Some bodybuilders have been known to take this to extremes, being reluctant to walk anywhere in case they burn off hard-earned muscle mass on the thighs, for instance.

Drug Abuse

The other, more worrying, kind of extremism one may encounter in gyms where body-builders and powerlifters train is drug abuse. Anabolic steroids are the most widely used drugs for building muscle mass and putting on muscular bulk, but they can have disastrous physical side effects such as kidney failure, liver damage, impotence and sterility, and unpredictable psychological side effects such as increasing aggressive tendencies to the point of complete loss of control, something totally at odds with what training in combat sports and martial arts aims to achieve. Some members of the bodybuilding fraternity argue that everyone should be allowed to use the drugs as the benefits are obvious, and if everyone was using them it would make for equal competition. But there is no question that these drugs can have a long-term adverse effect on one's health. There is no excuse for taking them in combat sports and they are outlawed in most amateur and professional forms. The steroid user in the context of a combat sport is nothing more than a cheat, seeking an unfair advantage. Legislation was introduced in England in 1988 to make trafficking in steroids illegal and punishable by a 5-year gaol sentence in a bid to discourage their use.

If you are the kind of person who cannot resist a bit of competition, you should ideally train with partners roughly your equal in terms of strength, weight and motivation. If your goals are the same, then your training is likely to be much more productive. Three is the ideal number for a training group, especially when training with heavy weights and employing movements like the squat and bench press, as two can act as spotters while one works, a big plus from a safety point of view. More than 3 working in a group will tend to slow things down too much as rest periods between sets become more prolonged. If your training partners are also friends, the effectiveness of the training often increases since it becomes an enjoyable social event rather than a monotonous, hard slog. A bonus is that trainees in a group are less inclined to fail to turn up, being reluctant to let each other down.

MYTHS

It is necessary at this point to dispel certain myths about weight training, the commonest being that weights make you tight and slow you down. Another myth is that when you stop doing weight training, the muscle gained turns to fat. The other great objection from the martial arts world has always been that if you rely on strength you will not be able to develop the necessary technique and skills, and although you may have some early successes, later, when you fight someone just as strong, you will lose through inferior technique. The fact is, the stronger and fitter a fighter is, the easier it is to skill train, and many taking up martial arts and combat sports lack the necessary basic strength to be really effective.

As for weight training making you muscle-bound, again it is a question of making sure that your training is correctly balanced so that your suppleness does not deteriorate. Stretch the whole body for 10 minutes before and after each session and you should find that exactly the opposite happens: you can actually use weight training to improve your flexibility. Such stretching will compensate for any tightening effect that results from heavy weight training.

As far as muscle turning to fat goes, that is a physiological impossibility. What does happen to some people is that they stop training completely and take no pains to modify their diet, in many cases eating and drinking more than when they were training. The unexercised muscle then begins to atrophy and shrink and fat deposits begin to occur all over the body. This is accelerated by inactivity as the body's metabolic rate slows down and fewer calories get burned up in daily life and are stored as fat.

The Training Programme

Standardised bodybuilding programmes are only really suitable for fighters if their overriding concern is to put on muscular weight. This necessitates a competition-free period of at least 6 months in which to concentrate exclusively on that, including attention to those aspects of bodybuilding that take place outside the gym such as nutrition and recuperation.

Unfortunately, despite the proliferation of gymnasiums, health clubs and fitness centres, there is a distinct shortage of knowledgeable coaching on the subject of specialised weight training for improved sports performance. This is one of the problems the fighter encounters when he goes to a gym and asks for a training programme. The instructors are almost invariably bodybuilders or physical education teachers who, while expert in their fields, generally have little understanding of what training in a combat sport entails. A weight-training programme for any combat sport has to be balanced, taking into account the individual's workload in its entirety; it has to accommodate and complement his other training, not replace or conflict with it. In addition, despite underlying scientific principles, there is much conflicting information about what is effective and ineffective, safe or unsafe.

On the subject of strength training, sources of information contradict one another in many important aspects. The full deep squat, for instance, is condemned by many as being a dangerous exercise likely to cause damage to the knees and lower back; other equally authoritative sources regard it as the absolute bedrock of any strength training or bulk building programme.

A similar situation exists with regard to the bench press, power clean and dead lift, and faced wth choosing which exercises to include in your workouts, you can end up thoroughly confused. Ultimately the only way to determine an exercise's suitability is to try it and see what effects it has on you: if it feels good, do it! The rules are mutable. Training that makes one person flourish will wither another. It is fair to say, however, that anyone who already has knee problems should not do full squats as there is a strong probability that the exercise will aggravate them. Similarly, anyone with back problems should be aware of the dangers inherent in heavy power cleans, squats and dead lifts. On the other hand, the sensible use of these exercises along with certain assistance exercises can clearly strengthen weak, injury-prone areas, so it is really a matter for individual assessment and experiment. A 3-month trial period should be allowed for an effective assessment of an exercise's suitability.

Correct technique when training with weights is vital if steady progress is to be made without injury. Equally important is mental flexibility and the ability to adapt your training: listen to your body at all times and do not make unrealistic demands upon it; injury can be avoided if it is anticipated. If you suffered a knock in training, a kick in the thigh while practising karate, or a jarred shoulder doing judo the night before, it would be folly to attempt a personal best in the gym the next day in the squat or bench press. Regularly attempting personal best lifts is in fact inherently dangerous and many coaches argue that maximum single repetition lifts are not worth the effort. A maximum single can be a great confidence-builder, and increasing your personal best in the bench press from 135kg (300lb) to 150kg (330lb) in 3 months undoubtedly reinforces faith in the effectiveness of your training, but the maximum single ought not be attempted every session: it demonstrates strength rather than develops it.

As a general guide, if you cannot do 3 repetitions with a weight it is too heavy to be useful as a training weight. It is important to remember that one huge maximum effort at lifting a weight has little relevance to your actual sport. If you are not a powerlifter it is not worth the risk. Of course, an occasional attempt at a personal best is necessary to effectively determine current strength levels or assess the extent of improvement in a particular area. On such occasions you should feel fresh and always observe strictly correct exercise form. Attempting a maximum poundage when fatigued is definitely not recommended.

Another important aspect of injury avoidance is the warm-up. Going into a gym and lifting heavy weights straight away is dangerous and foolish. Some bodybuilders favour an approach they label 'high intensity' but which is inherently dangerous from an injury point of view and psychologically almost impossible to sustain – physically, too, if steroids are not being used! Ten minutes' warming up with some stretching, skipping, a few minutes on an exercise bike or some callisthenics, is the right approach. Be careful not to burn up all your energy in warming up though, especially if you are training for power, when you need to be reasonably fresh.

The Set System

Just as repetition is at the heart of training methodology in martial arts, so it is in weight training. Basically, in a weight-training session the amount of work that is to be done is broken up into sets of repetitions. Say, for example, a trainee wanted to do 30 reps of the bench press. Using only 45kg (100lb) he could probably do one set of 30. However, this would be of little value for developing strength since the weight would be too light and have only an endurance effect on the muscles. Increasing the weight to 70kg (150lb) he would probably find it necessary to stop after 10 reps and give the muscles a rest before continuing, in which case he might do

3 sets of 10, with about a minute's rest between sets. If he increased the weight to 80kg (180lb) he might find he could only do 5 reps, in which case to achieve his original target of 30 he would need to do 6 sets. Taking the principle still further, 10 sets of 3 with 90kg (200lb) would be the logical conclusion. Although the total number of reps is the same, the workload has doubled from the first workout. This illustrates the principle and value of training in sets, which allow heavier weights to be handled with consequent increases in strength, speed and power which would otherwise not be feasible.

Of course, how many repetitions you can do with a given weight is determined by how strong you are and the weight being handled. What weight you train with depends upon what you are training for, and recent Soviet research into the prerequisites of strength training has interesting implications for the combat sportsman. To put it simply, the research shows that training affects the trainee in the following way:

1. Training with less than 50 per cent of your maximum will only develop stamina and not absolute strength, as the training action will invariably be too ballistic.
2. Training with weights that range from 50–80 per cent of maximum primarily develops speed.
3. Training with weights that range from 80–95 per cent develops speed in conjunction with strength.
4. Training with weights of 95 per cent of maximum develops strength only.

These maximums refer to the maximum weight that can be handled for one repetition, so a powerlifter capable of a single 180kg (400lb) bench press wanting to train at 95 per cent of his maximum would have to lift 170kg (380lb). Consequently he would initially at least once a week need to do 10 sets of 3, since it is highly unlikely that he could do more reps with such a heavy weight. It requires no great cognitive leap to infer from this that the different needs of martial artists require quite different approaches. The non-contact karateka primarily concerned to develop the speed to beat the opposition to the punch should be training in the 50–80 per cent range, whereas the judoka attempting to develop an effective ura-nage (a pick-up throw requiring considerable explosive strength and coordination) should work in the 80–95 per cent range.

What does this mean in practical terms? Take the case of a single exercise: the squat. A karateka capable of, say, a single maximum repetition with 90kg (200lb) in the squat would, adhering to the idea of progressive resistance, begin training with 3 sets of 10 reps with only 45kg (100lb). Training 3 times a week, he would increase the weight by 5kg (10lb) after every third session. After 6 weeks he would be doing 3 sets of 10 with 70kg (160lb), or 80 per cent of his original maximum. Factors such as familiarity with the exercise and improved technique would also modify the notion of the personal best, and re-testing at this point would probably see a marked increase of at least 10 per cent (i.e. a 100kg (220lb) single repetition in the squat). The heavier judoka already capable of this, however, would commence training in the 80–95 per cent range doing 6 sets of 6 reps, starting the first week at 75kg (170lb) and adding 5kg (10lb) per week until after a further 4–6 weeks he is doing sets of 6 with 100kg (220lb), his original maximum lift in the exercise. His current maximum would by this time have gone up to about 115kg (250lb). The squat is rather a special case, since people who have not seriously trained in the exercise before make fairly rapid early gains then reach a plateau where improvement becomes a lot harder, and more specialised routines may become necessary. The average karateka or judoka, though, would have reached his real basic strength potential and would maintain good leg strength and speed by doing a maintenance routine only once a

week, or could opt to become still stronger and persevere with heavier weights, depending on how important a contribution he felt the training was making to his overall performance.

The apparently arbitrary nature of the number of sets and reps to be performed is pretty well established according to physiological responses to exercise and determined by working out the trainee's current absolute maximum in a given lift and then allocating a workload which is a percentage of that maximum. The number of reps done and the weight to be used are then calculated bearing in mind the functions of the training percentages listed above; 6 × 6 is common as a power-building routine whereas 3 × 10 is normally appropriate for improving speed and strength endurance. Remember, though, that the importance of the number of reps and sets is determined by the poundage as a percentage of your maximum. Muscle tone will improve to some extent whichever system is employed. Of course, the same methodology has to be applied to a whole group of exercises, since only doing one exercise would be of little value. A typical workout would then comprise 8–12 different exercises for the various muscle groups in order to have a whole body training effect.

More Pre-training Considerations

The only objection to the novice fighter weight training is that, given the rigorous demands of combat sports, weight training on top might result in overtraining. It can, however, be unreservedly recommended in off seasons, or when other demands prevent regular training in the dojo, as an alternative to losing condition. The ratio of weight-training sessions to actual dojo workouts has to be determined by need. A really unfit judo player, for instance, would be better off doing weights 3 times a week and judo only twice until he felt strong enough to compete in the dojo on more equal terms, then switching to 3 judo sessions and reducing the weight training to twice a week to maintain his strength gains. A very strong fighter, though, would be better advised to make good use of his strength by skill training and trying to develop the speed of his techniques, perhaps doing weights only once a week to maintain and monitor strength levels.

The use of heavy poundages without adequate foundation training can certainly be counter-productive. Heavy squats and power cleans can cause chronic muscular soreness if you try too much too soon and will undoubtedly cause a deterioration in your actual performance in the ring or on the mat. Attempting to practise or fight with any intensity in such a tired state is folly and invites injury. The way to proceed is to start with moderate weights and build up gradually.

The first step before embarking on a weight-training programme to supplement your other training is to define your goals. Why are you going to weight train? Do you want to get faster, stronger, heavier, lighter, fitter or some combination of these things? It is a lot easier to get somewhere if you know where you are going. Training specificity has to be considered along with phasing. It is more effective to train for one quality at a time and it is usually best to allocate blocks of time to those things you plan to train for. One popular approach is to spend 6 weeks concentrating on general endurance – longish runs followed by circuits, 6 weeks on local muscular endurance and strength, 6 weeks on power training, and finally, in the period close to competition, 6 weeks on speed and sharpening of techniques, with weights assuming a minor strength-maintenance role, maybe 1 or at most 2 sessions a week. Of course, you need to experiment to find out what produces the best results for you personally. The important thing is to strike the right balance of effort and training in the gym and in the dojo.

Naturally, the top-flight international competitor will have hugely different requirements to the middle-aged club dan grade who aspires only to being a bit fitter so he can get through sessions without running out of steam towards the end. Training with maximum poundages in weight lifting is highly anaerobic. Repetition squats with heavy weights, for instance, are totally gruelling. The body simply cannot supply enough oxygen to keep the muscles working, hence the intense feelings of breathlessness accompanying such an activity. Shuttle runs, too, produce an anaerobic effect and for the superfit can be done with weights held in the hands to put the body under real stress. Such high intensity work should be done only once or at the most twice a week, otherwise injury or at least overtraining will be a likely result.

SPECIFIC WEIGHT-TRAINING EXERCISES

The Big 4 weight-training exercises from the point of view of developing overall body power are the squat, bench press, dead lift and power clean.

The *squat* is the basis of most routines where the concern is to increase weight and strength, and is a fundamental movement for improving leg and back strength. Karate, kung fu and taekwondo students eager to increase the speed and power of their kicks can gain a lot from this exercise. Many top sprinters use it as a direct stimulus for increasing leg speed, an essential element in their sport. The trainee should invest in a proper pair of weight-lifting boots, which normally have a slightly built up heel and provide strong ankle support, and a body belt which provides support and protection for the lower back and abdomen. The belt is only really necessary when very heavy weights are being handled. For serious training, a set of squat stands or, even better, a squat rack from which to lift the weight down, is essential. Weights being used when squatting rapidly exceed what can be lifted overhead and lowered to the behind-neck position commonly employed, so attempting to train in a gym which does not have such equipment is something of a dead end. Similarly, the best type of bar for squatting is an Olympic bar and ought to be considered essential equipment.

Squatting stimulates and stresses the largest muscle groups in the body, those of the legs, including the gluteus maximus and quadriceps, and with regular training very heavy weights can be lifted. Increases in strength, power and weight tend to be marked through regular training but there are a number of potential drawbacks which vary from individual to individual. Some people experience intolerable lower back pain (the erector spinae muscles of the lower back tend to be the weak link in squatting, and serious lifters do special assistance exercises to condition these muscles); others find the exercise hurts their knees. The remedy for back pain is to prepare the muscles for the stress of squatting by doing lots of back raises and good morning exercises. Those who suffer from knee pain can try powerlifting knee wraps, but if the knee has been damaged in the past it is undoubtedly wiser to leave the squat alone and do heavy leg presses, leg extensions and curls to compensate. If in doubt, get medical advice. A less serious problem is pain caused by the weight of the bar digging into the back of the neck/shoulders. This is generally a result of taking the weight in the wrong place. The bar should rest across the trapezius muscles of the upper back, which act as padding, not on the axial vertebra of the neck where beginners tend to place it. Some people find wrapping the bar in a towel or foam rubber helpful, but in most cases this should not be necessary if the bar is correctly positioned in the first place.

Many lifters claim that when poundages in other exercises such as bench press or dead

lift begin to stick and progress stops, the answer can lie in increased intensity of training in the squat, which they feel to be the key to overall body strength and power. An unfortunate consequence of heavy squatting is chronic muscular soreness. Some stiffness, say the day after training or perhaps even two days afterwards, is normal and a sign that training was sufficiently hard to have had a positive effect, but painful stiffness lasting 4 or 5 days is a clear indication of overtraining in the sense that too much weight was used too soon.

There are various ways of performing the exercises but the basic version is the back squat. The bar is held across the shoulders behind the neck with the feet shoulder-width apart, and the lifter lowers himself by bending the legs, while keeping the back straight, until his thighs are parallel with the floor, or at a 90-degree angle. There is no real need to squat any deeper than that. Going right down as deep as possible has been blamed by numerous informed sources for causing a variety of knee problems. The main objection seems to be that the joint is simply not designed to cope with the stresses it is

Figs 64–6   The squat.

Fig 65

Fig 66

subjected to in the fully-stretched position of the deep knee bend and under the compressing force of the combined weight of the body and barbell.

For reasons of safety, there should be spotters on hand to help if you get into difficulties attempting to lift a weight. Two are required if you are lifting more than your bodyweight, and where heavy weights are being lifted a third is desirable. They need to be strong enough to take the weight if through fatigue or over-ambition you find yourself unable to straighten up with the weight in the course of a set. Never squat alone!

Important technical points to bear in mind are that once you take the weight from the rack and 'reverse out', you should lower yourself into position slowly, keeping the back as straight as possible and the head up. Lowering the head causes the back to bend forwards. This is a common fault which occurs in the performance of a set as the legs tire and the squatter tries to alleviate the strain on the thigh muscles by taking some of the weight on the lower back. This is to be avoided at all costs as it is very easy to injure the relatively weak back muscles when heavy weights are being handled. Keep the chin up and fix the eyes on some point well above head height to discipline yourself into maintaining good posture. Breathe in as you go down and out as you come up. Come up as fast and as forcefully as you like without sacrificing good form, but never drop down into a squat position with a loaded bar at speed as this is virtually guaranteed to have a traumatic effect on the knees. Remember, too, that it is potentially dangerous to squat with heavy weights when you are below par. if you are not supple in the hips and ankles and find the squat to be a mechanically uncomfortable movement, front squats using lighter poundages are an effective way to work up to the standard squat. They isolate the fronts of the thighs so less weight can be lifted, but they do discipline you into de-

veloping very good lifting posture which lays a better foundation for later heavier training. Some people find squatting with a block of wood under the heels helpful for maintaining balance as it reduces the tendency to lean or fall to the rear. One common practice which has come in for a lot of criticism is that of squatting on to a bench. The underlying logic of this is that if the lifter finds himself unable to rise he just sits on the bench, rather than getting trapped in the full squat position. The danger, though, is that the lower back is left supporting the weight alone. Shearing forces can be transmitted through the spinal column, which can result in severe back injury.

Finally, the exercise should take about 5–6 seconds per repetition, 2 actually to come up or lift the weight and 3–4 to lower yourself into the lifting position. A slow descent is doubly important since as well as avoiding potential injury it stores kinetic energy for a powerful lifting effort. This applies to all the weight-training exercises described in this chapter, except the explosive lifts like the clean and jerk.

The *bench press* is the yardstick by which most weight trainers measure their upper body strength. In fact it really only gives an indication of pushing power, but as a general power-building exercise for the shoulders, chest and upper arms it is probably unsurpassed. The mechanics of the exercise are very simple. You lie on the bench, which is normally fitted with stands for holding and receiving the weight, and keep your feet on the floor to ensure a stable lifting position. Take the weight off the stands, using a grip that in most cases ought to be slightly wider than shoulder width. Lower the weight slowly to your chest, breathing in as you do so. From the extended position the weight should travel in a straight line down to the chest, roughly in a line with the nipples. Breathe out as you lift the weight off your chest, keeping the head on the bench and the hips flat. The grip taken to do the exercise determines which muscles receive

Figs 67–8   The dead lift.

Fig 68

the greatest amounts of stress. A wide grip increases the stress on the pectorals and deltoids, but takes strain off the triceps. Conversely the narrow grip isolates and works the triceps harder, but as they are relatively small muscle groups, it is unrealistic to expect to handle as much weight with such a grip. Remember, too, that the wider the grip the less distance the weight travels, so it becomes mechanically more efficient to lift with a wide grip, even though it does place a lot of pressure on the wrists.

Variations on the basic grip, changing the spacing of the hands or occasionally reversing, can be useful for strenghtening weak areas and getting over sticking points, but it is also necessary sometimes to change the angle you press at, performing the exercise on an inclined or declined bench. Dumbbells can also be used in place of the Olympic bar and have the advantage that they allow a greater range of movement, although initially they are harder to position and control and tend to wobble about more when tiredness sets in.

The *dead lift* is considered among powerlifters to be the exercise that sorts out the men from the boys. It develops great strength in the legs, lower back, shoulders and grip. Technique is very important if heavy weights are to be safely handled, but is very straightforward. The exercise involves bending the legs, keeping the back as straight as possible and grasping the bar with two hands, then straightening up, pulling the bar to waist level by using the power of the legs and back. With heavy weights it is necessary to hold the bar with the hands reversed, one palm facing outwards, the other inwards towards the body. This prevents the bar from rolling and causing the fingers to open when very heavy weights are being handled. Throughout the course of each lift the trainee should keep his head up and look up, not down at the bar. Once erect, pull the shoulders back to lock out. Taller individuals (who normally find the squat in particular to be very hard work) are at less of a disadvantage than their shorter training partners in this exercise than in many others.

The weak link in this movement is invariably the grip, and additional strengthening exercises must be done if it becomes a problem. These can include wrist curls, wrist rollers and reverse curls keeping the wrists cocked. The other problem areas can be the lower back; in order to strenghten it some people do the exercise with straight legs, but this is an assistance exercise in its own right (the stiff-legged dead lift) and the weight handled is of necessity much lighter, and the technique should not be confused with the regular dead lift.

The *power clean* is a gross power-building exercise which can be particularly useful to judo players who want to develop greater pulling power. Like the squat, it develops all-round body power, especially in the legs and back. High repetitions with this exercise have a shattering effect and can be recommended to anyone keen to develop anaerobic fitness, but good technique is vital in order to avoid possible injury. The starting position is with the feet shoulder-width apart, standing over the bar which is on the floor. Crouch down, bending the knees but keeping the back as straight as possible, and take a comfortable grip on the bar (overgrasp). The hands should be equidistant from the ends of the bar for balance. Keep the head up and straighten the back until the arms straighten, and begin to lift immediately by driving with the legs and pulling the bar high.

As the bar reaches chest level you have to relax and drop underneath it so that the bar finishes resting across your upper chest. Most people make the mistake of trying to get the arms into the lift too soon. The initial drive of the lift should come from the legs and back, the arms only really coming into it as the weight passes the waist level and they accelerate the bar to chest height. It can help to think of them as flexible hooks through which you transmit the power of the

Figs 69–70   The dumb-bell power clean.

Fig 70

legs and back. Keep the head up throughout and pull the elbows high, so that you can more easily get underneath the bar at the crucial moment. Form is very important, remember: bend the legs, back straight, head up and elbows high. Avoid letting the legs straighten first and lifting with a rounded back as even medium weights will rapidly give you a sore back and sooner or later damage the lumbar region.

The descent phase is equally important from the point of view of avoiding injury, and it is a good idea to lower the bar from the chest and catch it at the thighs, rather than trying to lower it directly to the floor, as this once again throws excessive strain on the back. Most gymnasiums do not have an Olympic lifting area and take a very dim view of people dropping heavy weights on their floors – another reason for learning the correct technique.

Apart from increasing general explosive power, this exercise greatly strengthens the trapezius area which is so important to conditioning the neck to absorb the shock of blows to the head, such as occur in boxing or kickboxing. Judoka, too, benefit, since the neck and lower back areas are subjected to all sorts of stress in training and competition. The legs get worked well by this exercise, so its application for karate and taekwondo is apparent. Never attempt a set of heavy power cleans if the legs are tired from running or other heavy exercise, since the stress will tend in those circumstances to be thrown on to the lower back. Any soreness of the lower back muscles can be taken care of by doing regular sets of back raises, ideally to begin and end each session where power cleans are performed.

SUPPLEMENTARY OR ASSISTANCE EXERCISES

This is not an exhaustive list but describes most of the major exercises that can be done using weights not already mentioned, that are useful for combat sports.

Curls Can be done with dumb-bells or a barbell. Primarily used to develop the biceps muscles, though the forearms are also affected. It is important to keep the elbows tucked in throughout the exercise otherwise the shoulders begin to do the work instead of the biceps.

With a barbell simply pick up the weight undergrasp so that you are standing up straight with the back of the hands at about mid-thigh, feet shoulder-width apart. Breathe in as you lift, curling the weight from the hanging position until it is level with the collar bones, and breathe out as you lower it back to the starting position. Avoid cheating-style movements where you swing the body to get the weight moving, and keep strict form. To really isolate the biceps the exercise can be done with the back to a wall or using a preacher bench, which has the effect of preventing the elbows from moving, forcing the biceps to do all the work. Reversing the grip to an overgrasp puts the emphasis on the outside head of the biceps and forearms, the exercise is then known as a reverse curl.

Curls can also be done using dumb-bells. Alternate arm curls are particularly effective, lifting with one arm as you simultaneously lower with the other. Dumb-bell curls can also be performed seated on an inclined bench. Setting the bench at a 30–60 degree angle changes the leverage and isolates the biceps still more.

Pull-downs Are normally done on a lat pull-down machine. The muscles worked include the latissimus dorsae, teres major and biceps (particularly if a close grip is employed). The exercise should be performed sitting on a bench or kneeling on one knee, without bending forwards or leaning backwards. Simply reach up and grip the bar in the arms extended overhead position and pull it down, inhaling as you do so until it touches the chest.

Figs 71–3   The barbell curl.

Figs 72

Fig 73

Exhale as you slowly allow it to return to the overhead position. A variation which allows the upper back to be worked very effectively is to pull the bar down to the back of the neck.

Lateral raises Performed with dumb-bells, this exercise works all three heads of the deltoid muscles. Stand, feet shoulder-width apart, with the arms straight, dumb-bells in front of you. Using only the shoulder muscles lever the weights overhead, keeping the arms straight throughout 360 degrees, until the backs of the hands meet overhead. Lower the dumb-bells until they meet in front of the body; that constitutes one repetition.

Triceps push downs Can be performed on a multigym to develop the triceps muscles. Simply grip the bar overgrasp and pull it to your chest. Push down, exhaling as you do so, until the arms straighten. Keep the elbows fixed against the midsection otherwise the chest and shoulder muscles share the workload.

Incline press Performed on an inclined bench with either barbell or dumb-bells. Isolates the upper chest and deltoids. The only difference to bench press is that the lift is performed at an angle. Increasing the angle increases the difficulty of the exercise, as more weight has to be taken by smaller muscle groups as you approach the vertical. About 45 degrees is ideal for working the upper pectorals. Dumb-bells increase the range of movement at the shoulder (since there is no bar which prevents the weight going lower when it stops at the chest). The alternate arm inclined dumb-bell press is especially recommended for sports which use punching movements, since it allows full extension of the shoulder joint.

Decline bench press This exercise is the reverse of the above since it throws more of the weight on to the lower chest muscles and many people find that they can actually lift more than in the bench press. Like the above, it is a useful movement to introduce into a routine for variety and when sticking points occur in the regular exercise.

Leg press There are several types of leg presses. Some require the trainee to get under a plate loaded with weights and, lying on their back, push up. Others allow a seated position to be taken, sometimes pushing straight out. Still others allow the weight to be pushed in an inclined plane of about 45 degrees.

Leg extensions Performed seated on a leg machine, or, if not available, on a bench wearing iron boots which strap on to the ankles. The quadriceps are effectively worked. A useful exercise for strengthening the muscles around the knee and helping to prevent injury. Can be useful for remedial purposes, but consult your doctor or physiotherapist first.

Leg curls Performed on the same apparatus as the previous exercise but in the prone position. You lie face down, your thighs on the bench and place your lower legs under the cushioned limb of the leg machine, then bend the legs, pulling the feet towards the backside. A much neglected exercise, this is very good for the hamstrings and less visible but equally important muscles of the hips and groin. Provides much-needed balance to the muscle groups of the legs.

Calf raises Another often neglected but very important exercise, which helps condition the feet and ankles and keeps them supple and strong, reducing the risk and effects of injury.

Press behind neck A good power-builder for the shoulders, this exercise can improve flexibility in the shoulder girdle but should be

Figs 74–5   The press behind the neck.

Fig 75

used with caution if the shoulders or collar bone have been previously injured. Lift the bar above the head and lower it until it touches the back of the shoulders, then press it back up. Keep the wrists locked straight for an increased stretch.

Straight arm pull-over The pull-over is a favourite of javelin throwers and develops great strength in extension. Keeping the arms straight, makes it a leverage lift requiring considerable effort to lift even moderate weights. The trainee lies on a bench and presses the weight to arm's length. Keeping the arms straight he takes the weight back over his head, stretching the thorax. He then levers the weight back to the vertical position, keeping the arms straight throughout the movement.

Bent arm pull-over This is similar to the previous exercise, except that the arms are kept bent throughout and the weight passes close to the face. Much heavier poundages can be handled in this exercise than in the straight arm version.

Bent over rowing Primarily a back exercise for developing the latissimus dorsae and teres major. The biceps and forearms are also given some stimulation. Many people find this exercise gives them lower back problems and prefer to keep the head supported on a bench or use a rowing machine in preference to free weights. Feet shoulder-width apart, bend at the waist and bend the knees, holding the bar with the hands about shoulder-width. Pull the bar to your stomach, exhaling as you do so, hold it there for one second before allowing the arms to straighten and the weight to return to the hanging position. Keep the head up throughout the course of the exercise.

Split jerk This is excellent for developing speed and power as well as coordination. It is especially good for sport karateka, who need to drop into a stance and blast out a quick punch. It can be performed either by cleaning the bar to the chest or taking the weight off a set of stands to the ready position. From this position bend the knees, keeping the back straight, then drive up forcefully with the legs and thrust the arms vigorously overhead. Come up on to the balls of your feet as you do so and split the feet, landing in a fairly high split.

Upright rowing A good exercise for developing pulling power in the shoulders, stressing the front and rear deltoids and trapezius. Standing upright, grip the bar overgrasp with hands close together, allowing your arms to hang down straight in front of you. Inhale and pull, drawing the elbows up parallel with the ears and the weight up to the chin. Slowly allow the weight to return to the hang position to complete one repetition.

Shrugs Another trapezius exercise which can be done using a bar bell or dumb-bells. With the arms hanging straight simply lift the weight by shrugging your shoulders as high as you can. Try to touch your ears with them!

Back raises Sometimes called hyperextensions, these are an absolute must for people who want to avoid lower back problems, and this exercise is recommended for all combat sports practitioners. Begin by climbing on to the machine and holding yourself in the horizontal position, and fold your arms in front of you. Slowly lower your upper body by bending at the waist until you reach an angle of 45 degrees. Feel the back muscles stretch and return to the horizontal position, breathing in as you do so. If you have had a back problem, avoid the true hyperextension where you come up and arch the back. Keep the body at 180 degrees to the floor and hold the horizontal position for a second or two before going down by bending forwards again. Build up the repetitions and when you

can comfortably do 3 sets of 20, try clasping the hands behind the neck. Be sure to lift the head and look up as you lift yourself into the horizontal position so that the erector spinae muscles of the lower back get fully worked.

Abdominal board A piece of apparatus that can go on the floor or be hooked on to a ladder or wall bars in the gym for doing abdominal exercises. Inclined sit-ups where the board is placed at an angle (the steeper the angle the more severe the exercise) put a lot of stress on the stomach muscles and build abdominal strength. They are best performed with the knees kept bent. Leg raises can also be performed by reversing your position on the board, but like sit ups they are much tougher done on an incline.

WEIGHT TRAINING FOR INCREASED SPEED AND POWER

The Big 4 can be used as the basis for any strength and power-building routine by combining them with a variety of assistance exercises. In fact it is rarely necessary to train in both dead lift and power clean outside of competitive lifting circles, so really the Big 4 becomes the Big 3, you just have to decide whether to do dead lift or power clean. Assuming a maximum of 3 weight-training sessions a week, the following pyramid system can be employed for guaranteed power and strength gains. Assume a bench press maximum of 150 kilos or pounds, (it does not matter for the purposes of calculating percentages of a maximum effort), and perform the following schedule:

10 × 60	1 × 140
10 × 100	3 × 125
8 × 110	4 × 120
6 × 115	6 × 115
4 × 120	8 × 110
3 × 125	10 × 100

This kind of pyramid system can be applied to each major exercise. Although the weights and repetitions suggested are hypothetical, they are not beyond the bounds of possibility for the determined trainee. If training on Monday, Wednesday and Friday (or Tuesday, Thursday and Saturday), pyramid one exercise per session – say, the squat on Monday, the dead lift on Wednesday and the bench press on Friday. On the day when one of the Big 3 is not being pyramided simply do 3 × 8 or 5 × 5 with 80 per cent of maximum, or leave it out and do something else, repetition dips instead of bench press or leg press instead of squat. Do not be afraid of variety, it is a vital ingredient of progress. Also, keep a record of what you do and how you feel as a result. This is a good way to discover what is really effective for you personally. Thus Wednesday would see the trainee doing 5 × 5 with 120kg (265lb) in the bench press and applying the same formula to his squatting routine while using the pyramid system on the dead lift, for example. If dead lift and squat in a single session is too demanding it does no harm to alternate these exercises, say, doing dead lift Monday and Friday one week, only squatting on Wednesday, then doing squat Monday and Friday the next week, only dead lifting on the Wednesday.

One system that seems to work well for combat sportsmen involves doing 3 sessions a week but concentrating on a different aspect in each session. The first training session of the week revolves principally around bench press and upper body pushing power, the second on squat and leg power, the third on clean or dead lift and develops grip strength and pulling power. This system allows for the fact that most combat sportsmen will be doing arduous training of their own in dojos and on the track, so does not create impossible goals and allows time for recovery.

Monday
Warm up with 5–10 minutes' callisthenics and a little stretching
Bench Press: pyramid (as above)
Wide grip pull downs (overgrasp) 3 × 10
Seated dumb-bell incline press 3 × 10
Lateral raises with dumb-bells 3 × 10
Upright rowing 3 × 10
Barbell curls 3 × 10
Triceps push downs 3 × 10
Dead lift 3 × 10
To finish: 20 calf raises, 20 inclined sit ups and 20 back raises, repeated 3 times (total 60 reps of each exercise)
Warm down with stretching for a good 10–15 minutes

Wednesday
Warm up with 5–10 minutes' stretching and callisthenics
Squat pyramid system
Leg extensions 3 × 10
Leg curls 3 × 10
Bench press 3 × 8
To finish: 20 calf raises, 20 inclined sit ups and 20 back raises, repeated 3 times (total 60 reps of each exercise)
Warm down with stretching for a good 10–15 minutes

Friday
Warm up with 5–10 minutes' stretching and callisthenics
Power cleans (or dead lifts): pyramid
Bench press 3 × 8
Single arm bent over rowing with dumb-bell 3 × 10
Front squats 3 × 10
Bent arm pull-overs 3 × 10
Dumb-bell flys 3 × 10
To finish: 20 calf raises, 20 inclined sit ups and 20 back raises, repeated 3 times (total 60 reps of each exercise)
Warm down with stretching for a good 10–15 minutes.

9 Circuit Training with Weights

WEIGHT TRAINING FOR STRENGTH ENDURANCE

Brief but intense (it is typically suitable for athletes with at least 3 years' training in their chosen sport), this circuit was devised by David Starbrook, Britain's first Olympic silver medallist at judo, and is effectively a giant set consisting of a succession of exercises performed without any rests. It improves strength and fitness, specifically developing upper body and grip strength but without putting on weight. It is especially useful for judoka and wrestlers. In various forms it can be used to increase stamina, develop strength endurance, and lose weight. If you want to use it for all the foregoing and also to increase sheer strength, the overload principle has to be employed.

Fig 77 Completion of the front press.

Fig 76 Starting position for the front (military) press.

Fig 78 Starting position for the press behind the neck.

Fig 79 Final position for the press behind the neck.

Fig 81 Mid-position for the reverse curl.

Fig 80 Starting position for the reverse curl.

Fig 82 Completion of the reverse curl.

Fig 83   Bent over rowing; starting position.

Fig 84   Bent over rowing; final position.

Fig 85   Curl; starting position.

Fig 86   Curl; mid-point position.

Fig 87   Curl; final position.

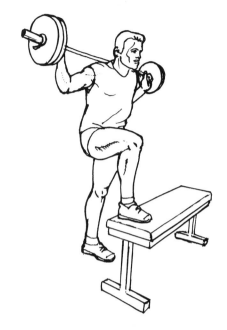

Fig 88   Step up; starting position.

Fig 89   Step up; completion.

Fig 90   Step down for next repetition.

Fig 91   Bent arm pull-over; starting position.

Fig 92   Bent arm pull-over; mid-point

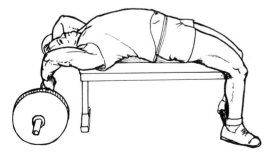

Fig 93   Bent arm pull-over; final position.

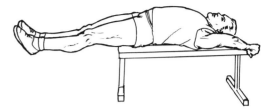

Fig 94   Leg raise; starting position.

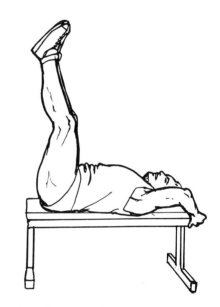

Fig 95   Leg raise; completion.

The circuit contains 8 exercises: the military press, French press, reverse curls, bent-over rowing, curls, step-ups, bent arm pull-overs and leg raises, to be done in that order. Each exercise is performed in a group of 10 repetitions except for leg raises, which are done in sets of 30. The step-ups entail 10 reps for each leg. These 8 exercises are done consecutively without any rests using a barbell, which is gripped at all times except when doing the leg raises. The exercises are repeated twice, for a total of 3 sets.

Although the tempo of the circuit is fast, good form should still be observed, especially on the bent-over rowing and curls where there is a tendency to swing the weights and get the back into it when fatigued. For improved strength endurance and cardiovascular fitness the circuit should be preceded by a run of 1½–3 miles. Even if you are trying to lose weight, more than 3 miles is not recommended as the circuit itself will rapidly deplete any glycogen reserves in the body, and if you overdo the running the circuit will be at best too slow and at worst you will be incapable of completing it. Aim to run at 6–8 minute mile pace (the lighter you are the faster you should do it), and the circuit itself should take 10–12 minutes. Select a weight equal to about one-third body weight initially. If you can do it in under 10 minutes increase the weight by 2.5kg (5lb) steps unitl it takes you at least that long to do it. Conversely, if it takes you longer than 12 minutes, the weight is probably too heavy so reduce it by 2.5kg steps until you can do it in under 12 minutes. When you get the circuit time down to 10 minutes, increase the weight by 2.5kg.

This weight increase makes a considerable difference to the difficulty of performance of this circuit, and bigger increases will result in a loss of form or possible failure to complete it. To accelerate weight loss and improve cardiovascular fitness, a jog after the circuit is suggested. Ideally this jog should be done immediately after the circuit itself, just as the circuit should immediately follow the run. Even a short rest after the run makes it considerably easier to perform and for an enhanced training effect any kind of rest should be avoided. The post-circuit jog is initially very hard and breathing is very difficult to control, but if you persevere you will find you actually recover more quickly by doing the jog, and get rid of the lactic acid build-up whilst running. After 5–6 weeks of this trainees often find themselves able to run rather than jog and literally raring to go as a result of their increased fitness. One of the advantages of this form of training is that it does not cause the chronic stiffness that often suggests that weights are incompatible with judo or wrestling. To succeed with this circuit training you must have a positive mental attitude; the equipment required is very basic – all you need is a barbell, a bench, and a lot of determination.

Experiment with the circuit, use it as you see fit. Try doing it 3, 5 and even 7 days a week, if you are using very light weights. Give it at least 4 and preferably 6 weeks, but no longer; after that time switch to a different system, you can always return to it at a later date. If you experience lower back pain (usually a result of failing to observe strict form) do some back raises (hyperextensions) but only come up to 180 degrees. Start with 3 sets

Fig 96 Starting and final position for the hyperextension or back raise.

Fig 97 Mid-point of back raise.

of 10 reps and build up to 3 × 20, and that should take care of it. If you get a sore neck (because of the step-ups) this can be avoided by padding the bar with foam rubber.

Ideally you should do the circuit in the morning or early afternoon if you intend to train on the mat the same day, as this gives you some recovery time. If exceptionally tired in practice, concentrate on timing, as technique will tend to deteriorate with fatigue, but remember that this is only temporary, and that when your fitness improves you will be vastly more effective. If alternating this circuit with judo or wrestling training, you should feel increasingly fitter and mat work should quickly become less stressful for you but much more so for your training partners. If you are doing the circuit every day and your mat work is suffering, after 3–4 weeks try dropping the weight to the original level you began training with – you will probably be amazed at how relatively easy it seems, which should convince you of your improvement in strength and endurance even though it may not be apparent on the mat, where you will initially suffer some performance deterioration from tiredness. After 6 weeks stop doing the circuit and take a week in which to just practise; the strength endurance improvement will be marked.

Although the above circuit is best suited to advanced trainers, the same principle can be applied for less well-conditioned athletes, using reduced weights, introducing rest periods, even initially reducing the number of sets to 2 instead of 3. There will still be a considerable training effect in a condensed period of time. Aerobic circuit training using weights is far from limited to this one type of training: the only real limiting factors being facilities, numbers and space.

CONDITIONING WEAK AREAS

Combat sports and martial arts need excellent all-round fitness and conditioning, but there are 3 areas which require more attention than most other sports-based programmes provide: the abdomen, the neck and the hands. The hands have to cope with terrific stresses and strains in most of the fighting sports, and it is important to work on developing finger and grip strength.

Grip strength can be developed in a number of ways and the fingers tend to get stronger as a consequence. The simplest exercise is to carry a sponge ball in the pocket and keep squeezing it. The Japanese gold medallist in gymnastics at the 1984 Olympics, Guchiken, developed his grip strength by simply hanging from the high bar for as long as he could, until he was able to hang for an hour without taking a break, at which point he decided that his grip was probably strong enough. Such training is probably way beyond most people, although its benefits are as visible, as the training itself is unappealing. Fortunately there are a number of methods and exercises for developing a powerful grip, some traditional, some modern, which are less monotonous, but which all demand determination. Most hand strengthening exercises involve going through the pain barrier, whether doing wrist curls for the forearms or pounding the makiwara to develop strong wrists and a compact fist.

Specialised abdominal exercises are necessary for most combat sports for a number of reasons. In activities where blows are landed to the body, a well-conditioned midsection is absolutely vital. A medicine ball can help to harden the stomach, but make sure you have a sensible training partner who is accurate – throwing wildly can lead to painful accidents if the ball hits too high or too low!

The trunk is also the source of much of the body's power when punching and kicking, and it needs to be at least as strong as the limbs. Even in sport karate where contact is penalised, the fighters need good stomach muscles for the occasion when a badly-controlled technique slams home. Those who neglect such conditioning do so at their peril. Judo players and wrestlers know the importance of working the abdomen hard, in order to be able to withstand the weight of another body falling on top of them and for blocking throwing attacks and escaping from hold downs. Consequently, a wide variety of abdominal exercises are recommended for best results, including all kinds of sit ups, crunches, leg raises, side bends and twists. Running is also good for toning these muscles.

The neck is an area of vital importance in combat sports: the strength of the neck is what largely determines the fighter's capacity to withstand being hit in the head. Wrestlers and judo men need strong necks for bridging in groundwork and to resist their opponents' efforts to bend them double. If a fighter gets thrown on his head, the stronger the neck the better the chance of avoiding injury. A head harness can provide good results, but one of the best exercises is the wrestler's bridge.

It is possible to do a simple circuit combining weights and callisthenics which, while providing a general workout for the whole body, concentrates on these areas. This aerobic circuit, consisting of 12 exercise stations, presupposes access to basic weight training equipment and a school gym, of the type where so many judo and karate classes are held.

Skipping
Rope climbing
Bent-leg sit-ups
Wrist roller
Shuttle runs
Leg raises
Wrist curls
Astride bench jumps
Wrestler's bridging
Deep press-ups on fingertips between benches
Reverse curls
Crunches

Fig 98   Starting position for the wrestler's bridge.

Fig 99   The basic exercise of the wrestler's bridge is performed by pushing up with the legs, raising the hips and suporting the weight of the body on the forehead in the arched position.

Fig 100   Wrestlers often perform strength and agility drills and spin from the arch through into this position.

These exercises can be grouped according to repetitions or time. A simple method is to do 1 minute on each exercise aiming to do as many good full reps as possible. After 1 circuit rest for 1–3 minutes depending on fitness, and repeat twice more in the same fashion. As there are 12 exercises and an average school gym can accommodate, say, 3 people on each station, a class of 36 is possible, and working on a time basis everyone works to their own level. Working on set numbers of reps can cause disorganisation, as people doing the exercises at different speeds may cause jams on certain stations. For the unfit who cannot work continuously for 1 minute at press-ups, for instance, the instructor can allocate achievable targets, such as 2 × 20 reps with a 10-second rest between sets, so the trainee works for 50 seconds at least. Gearing the circuit to meet the needs of individuals is the instructor's job, but it is vital that he set goals which are achievable.

Rope climbing of any kind is beyond many people yet Shozo Fuji, Japan's four-time world judo champion, could go up a rope using only one hand, with his feet apart! Strong students might be told to climb the ropes without using their feet, average students to use their feet, and weak ones just to hang on for as long as possible. Where weights are used there should be a choice of barbells for weak, average and strong trainees. Taking 2 seconds to lift and 4 seconds to lower the weight should mean the trainee performs 10 reps in each 1 minute block.

WEIGHT-TRAINING ROUTINES FOR KARATE AND OTHER STRIKING ARTS

The karateka and those of similar ilk should always bear in mind that while big muscles are impressive and it is undoubtedly satisfying to the ego to lift big weights, the relevance to the non-contact versions of the sport of being able to bench press 135kg (300lb) is questionable. Of course, in a full-contact or self-defence context the more power available the better, but for semi-contact it is important not to be sidetracked by irrelevances. The following are some of the more appropriate weight-training exercises for the karateka, organised into a circuit.

10 x split clean and split jerks with Olympic bar
10-20 sit-ups
10 × lunges with dumb-bells
10-20 leg raises
10 × kick back on leg press machine
10-20 crunches
10 × leg extensions
10-20 hanging knee rasies
10 × leg curls
10-20 sit-ups
10 × alternate arm dumb-bell press
10-20 leg raises
10 × lateral raises using dumb-bells
10-20 crunches
10 × dumb-bell curls
10-20 hanging knee raises

The circuit is then repeated twice more.

This is a particularly tough circuit for sorting out weak stomach muscles; on the abdominal exercises beginners should try 10 reps, intermediate trainers 15, and black belts 20. The really fit athlete who finds hanging knee raises too easy could do hanging leg raises, lifting his feet till they touch his hands where they are gripping the bar.

10 Fitness and Injury

Injuries are the bane of the combat sports-man and the very nature of his activities make them at some point all but inevitable. Being in top physical condition is one way to minimise the risk. The majority of injuries are not caused by single damaging incidents, but are stress related, often being a consequence of repeated punishment or cumulative stresses. For instance, the over-enthusastic student determined to train twice a day, who swims just prior to doing judo in the evening, is much more likely to twist an ankle or pull a muscle than the athlete who trained 8 hours earlier then rested and allowed his body to recover at least partially from the stresses placed on it by the earlier training session. Getting the balance of training right is a very important aspect in making progress. Always aim to go into your main training sessions – those that involve sparring or randori – fresh and raring to go.

The areas of the body most prone to injury tend to be the muscles and tendons around the joints, the knees, elbows, ankles, wrists and shoulders. Although any joint may be liable to injury given the strenuous nature of combat sports, the knee is probably the area that gives more trouble than any other. Initially this was thought to be because Westerners have stiff knee joints compared to Japanese and Koreans, who spend a lot of time sitting cross-legged on floors in the course of their daily life. Certainly limited flexibility of the knee joints makes injury more possible, but many Japanese, too, suffer knee injuries doing judo and karate. The activities are inherently stressful. As a result of the kicking techniques of karate and tae-kwondo where the leg muscles have to stop the kick as well as generate it, the muscles around the knee are subjected to severe stresses. Kicking into thin air is both commonplace and traditional but many instructors, realising that it can cause problems, advocate the use of less traditional training aids such as focus pads and kick bags to remedy the problem. It is particularly easy to strain things when tired or not warmed up.

Incorrect stretching technique can cause muscle pulls and tears, and ballistic stretching from cold and 'bouncing' to reach positions of full extension are not recommended. More scientific slow stretching methods are the order of the day, especially where 'old injuries' are involved. Overstretching prior to being fully warmed up or loss of balance are common factors in many training injuries. Providing the trainee warms up properly, the nature of training is gently progressive, and correct technique is learned, the possibility of injury is substantially minimised.

Many of the injuries incurred in training are of a minor nature perhaps needing only RICE – i.e. rest, ice, compression and elevation. Some will be more serious and will demand extensive rest and recuperation. Severe injury, especially if not properly treated in the first instance may put an end to all training for good.

No matter how skilful or experienced, no one is invulnerable and anyone can be unlucky. There are, though, certain negative factors which can contribute to injury and recognising them in advance can help to avoid problems. Quite often an injury in training will be the result of psychological factors such as sexual frustration, or dissatisfaction with work or other aspects of your personal life, which can lead to aggressive recklessness. When tired or off-colour, proceed with caution. Training after over-indulging in food, alcohol, tobacco or other drugs is inviting trouble.

There is an element of risk and excitement in any combat sport which should provide sufficient stimulation for the above excesses to hold no attraction. Certainly they are incompatible. An acceptance of the risk element inherent in combat-based activities should also develop a mature, practical attitude and an awareness of the importance of proper safety procedure. Unfortunately there is no universal agreement as to what constitutes the latter. Surveys have shown that in competition where the rules dictate the wearing of guards to groin, fist, feet, shins and head, the reduction in the frequency of injuries can be as much as 90 per cent. However, many traditionalists insist that pads encourage the very lack of control for which they are supposed to be compensating. The headguard in boxing and kickboxing is another controversial piece of safety equipment, with many arguing that it actually increases the danger of brain damage.

Adequate safety precautions are undeniably important, but so, too, is avoiding overprotectiveness. An activity like kickboxing is laden with danger, but that is undoubtedly part of its appeal: the greater the risk, the greater the thrill and the greater the sense of achievement when the challenge is met. It is to be hoped, though, that practitioners receive the guidance of mature individuals or develop sufficient maturity themselves to judge the dangers in a realistic fashion.

The psychology underlying sports injuries is fascinating. Lack of fitness can be a major contributor or source of potential injury, but why is someone unfit? The unfit fighter may lack time or motivation, or he may not have the necessary knowledge to work out a training programme and get himself fit. The novice may be injured shortly after starting the activity, but in such cases it will be the result of an accident due to a lack of proper preparation and supervision. But there are some who get themselves injured, or at times claim to be injured to escape the stresses of training. The traditional martial arts were a way of life, but nowadays trainees engage in activities like karate and taekwondo as adjuncts to their lifestyles, which in the modern world are inevitably much more stressful. Consequently there are periods when training lapses. As a result it is highly desirable to undertake self-monitoring when necessary and to be objective while making assessments of current levels of fitness and, indeed, finesse. The first thing to go when training lapses tends to be timing, and awkwardness after a lay-off may result in injury either to oneself or to one's training partner. If you know yourself, your mind as well as your body, and recognise your strengths and weaknesses, you will be much better prepared for your chosen activity, and much less likely to injure yourself or others.

Motivation is an important facet of the question, too. Controlled aggression is intrinsic in any combat sport. It can be described as a positive mental attitude, but in some cases fighters act over-aggressively to conceal apprehensions and misgivings. Fear is not too strong a word for what many feel just before going into action, sometimes even in the relative safety of the club training session. Churning stomach, shaky legs and twitching face muscles are just some of the common indications that the body's safety mechanisms are in working order. There will always be an element of fear in conflict situations, even when highly ritualised as in sports and martial arts. The crucial point is that you use that fear to provide a positive impetus to your efforts and do not succumb to it.

Injury can be real or imagined, and is sometimes used as an excuse to avoid stressful situations. Those lacking in confidence will often resurrect old injuries to escape the humiliation (as they perceive it) of being beaten by a higher grade or stronger member of their particular peer group, whilst they happily 'dish it out' to lower grades. The core of the problem is ego. The oriental arts were invariably group-oriented and in a sense egoless, whereas Westerners tend to be highly individualistic, frequently wanting to demonstrate their skills, rather than simply develop them. This kind of vanity can lead to conceited behaviour and a tendency towards bullying. The instructor should confront this kind of behaviour as soon as it manifests itself.

The commonest area of injury in combat sports, as already mentioned, is the knee. There are a number of reasons for this, some stemming from the joint's basic anatomical structure. The knee is basically a hinge joint but it also has to have a combination of flexibility, strength and stability to function as it must under the stress of training in a combat sport. Consequently various component parts become susceptible to injury.

One common problem is cartilage damage. Cartilage is a smooth, shiny, bluey-white substance which, while remarkably strong, is incapable of self-repair when damaged. It covers the ends of the femur and the fibula and tibia but is not particularly flexible, and when the knee is subjected to excessive torsional forces it may tear.

The bones inserting into the knee cap or patella are separated by the semi-lunar cartilages (so called because they resemble the shape of a half moon). These are of a different composition to the cartilage covering the ends of the bones, but similarly do not self-repair once damaged. They are prone to displacement rather than tearing, and providing there is little damage, can often be relocated through careful manipulation. As with most injuries, immediate attention is crucial and may save months of unnecessary pain or even permanent problems. In serious cases a displacement can be relocated surgically under anaesthetic.

Water on the knee is another common ailment but is in fact the body protecting an injury. The surfaces of the bones are separated by a film of fluid which lubricates and prevents tissue wear; however, in the event of an injury the volume of fluid increases dramatically in order to protect the joint from further trauma. The knee feels swollen, unstable and painful.

Ligaments are the binding which holds the joint together. They can be either torn completely or strained, and cause an instability in the knee which is probably the most common knee injury in combat sports. Multiple factors can contribute to this, but slipping and twisting the knee while it is in the bent position is the most usual cause. Once the joint becomes unstable the only course of action in most cases, with the exception of surgery, is to strengthen the overlaying muscle groups, hence the interminable static quads dished out by physiotherapists, and the presence of leg extension and curling machines in most professional football clubs, where twisted knees are equally common.

Although rest is necessary for recovery from most injuries, there are exceptions – for instance, runner's knee or chondromalacia patellae, where the front of the knee swells up. The muscles which finally straighten the knee are often left in an unexercised state as a result of sporting activities such as karate where the knees are kept in bent positions. With this particular ailment rest serves no useful purpose. There are various other tissues around the knee, including the bursae, capsule, fascia and fat pads. All of these can produce problems but are less common. As a general guideline, provided there is no excess swelling, pain or heat in the joint, it is better to exercise knees than to rest them.

Elbow injuries are common in martial sports. The types of injury vary considerably, ranging from damage caused by armlocks in sports like judo or bursitis caused by repeated locking of the elbows when punching air in some styles of karate and taekwondo. The elbow is generally considered as a simple hinge joint, but in fact it is more complex, comprising three joints: as well as the true elbow joint between the upper and lower arm, there are also the joints between the radius and the humerus and the radius and the ulna to consider. In addition, it connects to the wrist, shoulder and neck, so problems in any of these areas may be caused by compensation for stiffness or weakness elsewhere.

Warm-up exercises such as press-ups can greatly minimise the possibility of injury. Good muscle tone in the biceps and triceps also helps reduce the risk of injury, so a pulling exercise such as partner pull-ups can be beneficial. Uchikomi movements practising a throw such as seoi-nage are particularly suitable for this and tend to be a part of most club judo sessions anyway.

Armlock injuries tend to fall into 2 categories, depending upon the nature of the technique which has been applied. Straight armlocks cause compression damage similar to overextending with a punch, straining the tissues in the front and inside of the elbow. The bent armlock strains the muscles and ligaments around the outside of the elbow and may cause damage to the shoulder muscles in some cases. The great annoyance of an elbow injury is that it interferes with so many aspects of training. Weight training has to virtually stop, heavy weights being likely to aggravate the injury, and punching exercises, too, are greatly impaired. The triceps push down using light weights flushes blood into the damaged tissues and so is a very useful exercise for helping repair elbow injuries.

The ankles are easily injured in martial arts training and once damaged can become injury-prone unless a specific remedial strengthening routine is employed to prevent this. For a sprain the injury has initially to be rested and treated with ice. When the swelling goes down it is advisable to begin reconditioning the ankle as soon as possible. Running is not recommended since the jarring which takes place will invariably have an

Fig 101   Elbow injuries are common in judo where a lot of contests are decided by armlocks.

Fig 102   The potentially fatal head dive uchimata.

adverse effect on the injury. Ankle injuries in particular illustrate the importance of adaptability in a fitness training programme; switching from running to swimming or cycling as the main element in your cardiovascular conditioning ought to be an automatic course of action in the event of such an injury.

Calf raises can be very effective in re-stabilising damaged ankle joints by strengthening the surrounding muscles. Another device often employed by physiotherapists is a wobble board, which requires the athlete to stand on the injured leg, usually with the eyes shut, and maintain his balance, which can be a useful drill even without the board. When the joint feels recovered skipping can be introduced to prepare for the rigours of roadwork, although running on any hard surface should be avoided for at least a month after incurring the injury, to allow for complete recovery.

The neck is most likely to be damaged in sports like judo or wrestling rather than ka-

rate or kickboxing. Again, warm-up is an extremely important factor in avoiding injury. Grappling on the ground often sees fighters trying to bridge by arching the body and taking the weight on the head and neck, which is a necessary part of escaping from being pinned down, especially for wrestlers. The neck must be kept mobile and supple as well as strong.

Judo has seen numerous rule changes in an effort to reduce the number of neck injuries, which are potentially much more dangerous than limb injuries. The most famous example was the ban applied to head dive-style uchimata attacks. The uchimata is one of the most popular throws in judo and has ended hundreds of contests by the decisive ippon score that is the chief aim of the sport. Basically it involves turning the back on the opponent and driving the throwing leg up between his thighs so that he is scooped off the ground then turned by the action of the hands so that he falls flat on his back. Fre-

Fig 103　Women kickboxers fight just as hard as the men and take equally hard knocks.

quently the thrower almost performs a somersault when executing the technique. One consequence of the popularity of the technique was the development of powerful pick-up counterthrows. In response, uchimata specialists began doing the technique with more and more abandon and evolved a way of performing it which made it impossible to pick them up and counter, by making a sort of head dive. The powerful see-saw action of the body in the head dive uchimata made the technique virtually impossible to counter but not to block, and that was when the problems and the injuries started. Correct blocking technique resulted in the weight of both players being transferred to the neck of the one attempting the head dive, and there were reports of deaths as a result of the throw being attempted in this way. Consequently anyone making such an attack was rightly deemed by the governing body (the IJF) to be placing their own safety, possibly their life, at risk and instant disqualification for this technique was felt to be the only way to eradicate it from the sport.

Many players confident of their ability with the technique even now fail to see the danger; as a young man, so did I. However, my eyes were opened to the reality of the danger one day when I went to practise in the judo club Ippon Raul Calvo in Cadiz. No one entering the dojo could fail to notice a life-size photograph of a judoka which hung on the joseki wall next to a poem written in Spanish in the style of a Japanese haiku:

The life of the athlete
Forged through discipline,
hard work and training,
Broken by bad fortune.
We will remember him always. . .

The photograph and the poem, like the name of the club, commemorated Raul Calvo, a Spanish champion who had died in shiai from a broken neck from a head dive uchimata.

Concussion injuries caused by striking techniques are another area of concern and are best checked by an expert as soon as possible. In the event of any knock-out the victim should be seen by a doctor and if necessary have a skull X-ray.

Index